How to Dazzle at

MATHS CROSSWORDS

Book 1

Neale Blincoe

Brilliant Publications

We hope you and your class enjoy using this book. Other books in the series include:

Maths titles

How to Dazzle at Algebra	1 903853 125
How to Dazzle at Oral and Mental Starters	1 903853 109
How to Dazzle at Written Calculations	1 903853 117

English titles

How to Dazzle at Writing	1 897675 453
How to Dazzle at Reading	1 897675 445
How to Dazzle at Spelling	1 897675 47X
How to Dazzle at Grammar	1 897675 461
How to Dazzle at Reading for Meaning	1 897675 518

Science titles

How to Dazzle at Being a Scientist	1 897675 526
How to Dazzle at Scientific Enquiry	1 903853 15X

If you would like further information on these or other titles published by Brilliant Publications, please write to the address given below.

Published by Brilliant Publications
1 Church View
Sparrow Hall Farm
Edlesborough, Dunstable
Bedfordshire LU6 2ES

Tel:	01525 229720
Fax:	01525 229725
Website:	www.brilliantpublications.co.uk
E-mail:	sales@brilliantpublications.co.uk

Written by Neale Blincoe
Cover illustration by Lynda Murray
Printed in the UK by Alden Group Limited
© Neale Blincoe 2003
ISBN   1 903853 389

First published in 2003
10 9 8 7 6 5 4 3 2 1

Contents

Introduction

Dear teacher

Welcome to an innovative series of photocopiable maths crosswords. They will drastically cut down your preparation and marking time and will give your pupils differentiated maths work that's fun to do and really develops their numeracy skills.

All teachers know the importance of setting differentiated tasks, but the burden of marking three or more sets of answers is the main reason why it is done so infrequently in schools. Well, your problems are over!

This book contains five sets of maths crosswords. Each set has eight different crosswords (roughly corresponding to the National Curriculum levels and ranging from Level 1 to Level 7). Now that's what I call differentiated!

The harder ones have lots of questions, whilst

the easy ones have much fewer. This means you can keep the whole class happy, since everybody will be doing something fun that they can achieve at!

They cover all numeracy topics, have several amusing and trivia questions and are ideal for using as numeracy starters, classwork, revision and homework, and cover lessons for just about every class in a high school (as well as the top years of junior school).

The best thing about them, though, is the fact that each set have exactly the same answers, so the whole class's work can be marked in class quicker than you can say Rumpelstiltskin! Answers are given on pages 44–48.

You have found yourself an outstanding resource and I guarantee that your ability to deliver extremely effective and almost relaxing lessons will be enhanced considerably.

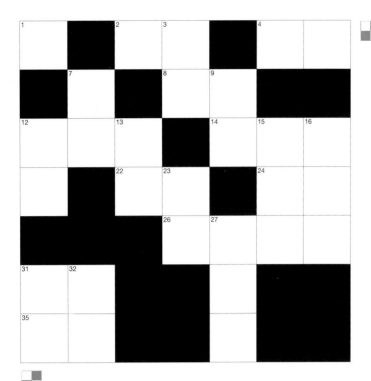

Crossword 1
Level 1

make sure you find all 4 decimal points

Clues across

1. ½ + ½ + 6
2. 7 + 7 + 7
4. (Number of sides in a rectangle x 2) + 2
8. (5 x 2) + 57
12. Three snakes, Sid, Sammy and Suzy, are measured. They are 46.9cm, 57.9cm, and 55.8cm. What is the biggest length?
14. What's the smallest amount of money? a) £0.32, b) £0.45, c) £0.12, or d) £0.57.
22. The number of sides in a triangle + 24
24. What is next in this sequence? 1.6, 1.5, 1.4, 1.3
26. Write out six thousand, one hundred and forty-six in figures
31. Is 53.9 closer to 53 or 54?
35. (8 x 10) + 6

Clues down

3. The age you need to be to leave school in England
7. How many halves make a whole one? Now add 25 to the answer.
9. 10 sweets are shared between 2 people. How many do they get each? Now add 65 to the answer.
12. 21 + 10 + 10 + 10
13. 99 – 4 – 3
15. 100 + (7 x 2)
16. Sid the snake had a son. He measured 22cm and 6mm. How can you write this in cm? Is it a) 21.6cm, b) 22.6cm, or c) 23.6cm?
23. 8 chocolate bars were shared between 2 people. How many did they get each? Now add 72.
27. Is 14 x 10, a) 120, b) 140, or c) 160?
31. 50 + (2 x 4)
32. Find the missing number: ? + 2 = 48

Crossword 1
Levels 1 & 2

make sure you find all 4 decimal points

Clues across

1. ½ + 6 + ½
2. 14 + 14 − 7
4. (Number of sides in a rectangle x 2) + 2
8. (3 x 3) + 57 + 1
12. Three snakes, Sid, Sammy and Suzy, are measured. They are 46.9cm, 57.9cm and 55.8cm. What is the biggest length?
14. What's next in this sequence? 0.08, 0.09, 0.10, 0.11
22. The number of sides in a triangle + 24
24. What is 0.9 + 0.3? Is it a) 1.1, b) 1.2, or c) 1.3?
26. Write six thousand, one hundred and forty-six in figures
31. Is 53.9 closer to 53 or 54?
35. 60 + 10 + 10 + 6

Clues down

3. The age you need to be to leave school in England
7. How many halves make a whole one? Now add 25 to the answer.
9. 10 sweets are shared between 2 people. How many do they get each? Now add 65 to the answer.
12. (7 x 3) + 10 + 10 + 10
13. 100 − 5 − 3
15. (10 x 5) + 50 + 14
16. Sid the snake had a son. He measured 22cm and 6mm. How can you write this in cm? Is it a) 2.26cm, b) 22.6cm, or c) 22.8cm?
23. (12 sweets shared between 3 people) + 72
27. 14 x 10 (Hint, 13 x 10 = 130)
31. 3 + 4 + 5 + 6 + 40
32. Find the missing number: ? + 4 = 50

How to Dazzle at Maths Crosswords Book 1

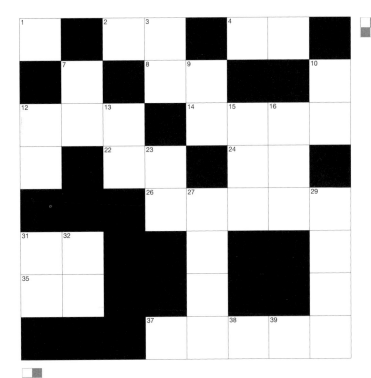

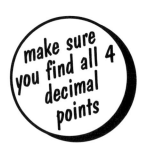

make sure you find all 4 decimal points

Clues across

1. ½ + 6 + ½
2. 14 + 14 − 7
4. (Number of sides in a rectangle x 2) + 2
8. (3 x 3) + 57 + 1
12. Sammy the snake was 57cm and 7mm long. We could say he was 57.7cm. His twin brother Sid was 2mm longer. How could we write his length with a decimal?
14. 125 is in between 124 and 126. What's in between 0.124 and 0.126?
22. The number of sides in a triangle + 24
24. 0.8 + 0.3 = 1.1. What is 0.9 + 0.3?
26. Write in figures sixty-one thousand, four hundred and sixty-one
31. Is 53.9 closer to a) 53 or b) 54
35. Find 50% of £6. Now add £83 to it. (Remember, 50% is the same as a ½)
37. 10,000 + 40,000

Clues down

3. The age you need to be to leave school in England.
7. How many halves make 3 whole ones? Now add 21 to the answer .
9. 4 + (12 ÷ 2) + 60
10. A triangle has angles 65° and 100°. What is the other angle? (Hint, all three add up to 180°)
12. (3 x 7) + 10 + 10 + 10
13. 100 − 5 − 3
15. (10 x 5) + 64
16. What's next in this sequence? 21.8, 22.0, 22.2, 22.4
23. (12 divided by 3) + 73 − ½ − ½
27. 14 x 100 (Hint, 13 x 100 = 1,300)
29. 1,354 + 3 + 2 + 1
31. The chance of Michael Owen being injured for the next International is 42%. What's his chance of being fit?
32. Find the missing number: ? + 4 = 50

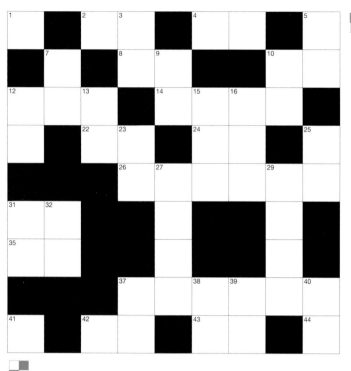

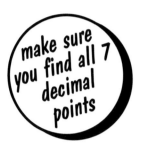

Crossword 1
Levels 2, 3 & 4

make sure you find all 7 decimal points

Clues across

1. A prime number can be divided only by 1 and itself. Which of these is prime? a) 6, b) 7, or c) 8.
2. $14 + 14 - \frac{1}{2} - \frac{1}{2} - 6$
4. (Number of sides in a pentagon) x 2
5. Number of faces on a dice
8. 3 squared + 58 *(Hint, squared means x itself)*
10. 2 x 2 x 2 x 2
12. 50 + 7.9 *(Hint, do 50 + 7 whole ones, then add the .9)*
14. What's in between 0.124 and 0.126? *(Hint, what's in between 124 and 126?)*
22. The number of sides in a triangle + 24
24. 0.3 x 4 *(Hint, do 3 x 4 then put the point in)*
25. What do you add to the 1st number in each coordinate to get the 2nd number? (0,1), (1,2), (2,3), (3,4)
26. Write in figures, six hundred and fourteen thousand, six hundred and twelve
31. 53.9 to the nearest whole number
35. Find 25% of £8. Now add £84 to the answer. *(Hint, 25% is a ¼)*
37. Half a million written in figures
42. (Area of a rectangle 2cm long and 4cm wide) + 16
43. The biggest pound note in England

Clues down

3. The age you need to be to leave school in England.
5. Number of sides in 22 triangles
7. How many thirds make up 2 whole ones? Now add 21 to that answer.
9. $(21 \div 3) + 13 + 50$
10. A triangle has angles 65° and 100°. What is the other angle? *(Hint, there are 180° in a triangle)*
12. −2 + 53
13. 100 − 8
15. (10 x 5) + 64
16. Is 22.57 closer to 22.6 or 22.7?
23. (12 divided by 3) + 72
25. A dozen
27. 14 x 100 *(Hint, 13 x 100 = 1300)*
29. 136 x 10 *(Hint, 137 x 10 = 1370)*
31. The chance of Michael Owen being injured for the next International is 42%. What's his chance of being fit.
32. Find x, if x + 3 = 49 *(Hint, do the opposite of + 3 to the 49)*
37. (Double 25) + 4
38. 0.9 − 0.4
39. James Bond is _ _7 *(Now put a decimal point in the middle of those two missing numbers.)*
40. 0.3 x 3 *(Hint, do 3 x 3 and put the point in)*
41. 7✈ − 6✈ = ?✈

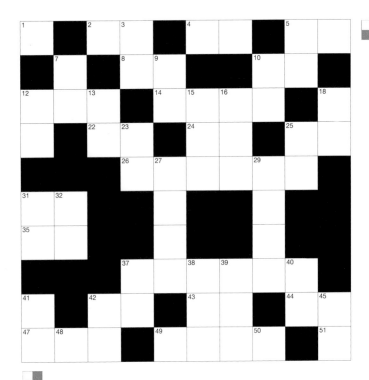

Crossword 1
Levels 3, 4 & 5

make sure you find all 8 decimal points

Clues across

1. The next prime number after 5 *(Hint, it has two factors, 1 and itself)*
2. The number of days in February – 7
4. (Number of sides in a pentagon) x 2
5. (2 x 6 x 2) + 38
8. 3 squared + 57 + 1
10. 2 x 2 x 2 x 2
12. 50 + 7.9 *(Hint, do 50 + 7 whole ones, then add the .9)*
14. What's in between 0.124 and 0.126 *(Hint, what's in between 124 and 126)*
22. The number of legs on a tripod + 24 *(Hint, what shape do you know with 'tri' in it?)*
24. 0.3 x 4 *(Hint, do 3 x 4 then put the point in)*
25. In any of these coordinates, what do you add to the x part to get the y part? (0,15), (1,16), (2,17), (3,18) *(Hint, the x part is the 1st number)*
26. Write six hundred and fourteen thousand six hundred and twelve in figures
31. 53.9 to the nearest whole number
35. If 50% of something is 43, what's the total? *(Hint, 50% is a half)*
37. Half a million
42. Area of a rectangle 6cm long and 4cm wide
43. The biggest pound note you can get
44. (16 x 2) + 60
47. (The perimeter of a square of length 2cm) + 124
49. £87.00 + £1.70

Clues down

3. The age you need to be to leave school in England
5. Number of sides in 22 triangles
7. How many thirds make up 9 whole ones?
9. Number of senses in the human body, e.g. smell + 65
10. A triangle has angles 65° and 100°. What is the other angle? *(Hint, there are 180° in a triangle)*
12. The temperature at night is –4°C and in the morning it's 3°C. Find the increase. Now add 44.
13. 100 – 8
15. (10 x 11) + 4 *(Hint, 10 x 12 = 120)*
16. Is 22.57 closer to 22.6 or 22.7?
18. Half a century + 5
23. (18 divided by 3) + 70
25. A dozen
27. 14 x 100
29. 136 x 10 *(Hint, 137 x 10 = 1370)*
31. The chance of Michael Owen being injured for the next International is 42%. What's his chance of being fit?
32. Find x, if x – 37 = 9 *(Hint, do the opposite of – 37 to the 9)*
37. (Double 25) + 4
38. 58cm in metres *(Hint, 56cm = 0.56 metres)*
39. 0.03 + 0.04
40. 0.3 x 3 *(Hint, do 3 x 3 and put the point in)*
41. 7🖰 + 4🖰 = ?🖰
42. 66 divided by 3 *(Hint, do 3s into 6 first)*
45. (⅓ of 90) + √4 – √9

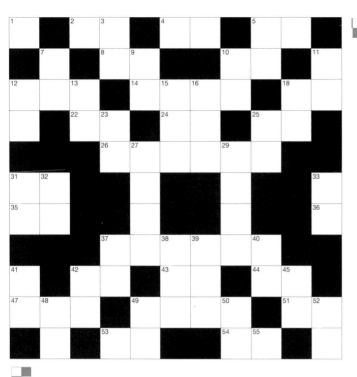

Crossword 1
Levels 4, 5 & 6

make sure you find all 10 decimal points

Clues across

1. The 4th prime number *(Hint, the 1st is 2)*
2. The number of days in February – 7
4. (Number of sides in a pentagon) x 2
5. 1m – 38cm (give your answer in cm)
8. 8 squared + 2 + 1
10. 2 x 2 x 2 x 2
12. 12.3 + 45.6 *(Hint, do 123 + 456 and then put the point in)*
14. ½ of 0.25 *(Hint, do ½ of 25 and then move the point)*
18. (10 x 5) + √16
22. The volume of a cube 3cm long, 3cm wide and 3cm high
24. 0.3 x 4 *(Hint, do 3 x 4 then put the point in)*
25. The coordinates (0,15), (1,16), (2,17), (3,18) all lie on the line y = x + ? *(Hint, what do you always add to the x part to get the y part of the coordinate?)*
26. Write six hundred and fourteen thousand, six hundred and twelve in figures
31. 53.6 to the nearest whole number
33. 1% of 800
35. If 50% of something is 43, what's the total?
36. 4 ÷ (the number of sides in a quadrilateral)
37. Half a million
42. Area of a rectangle 6cm long and 4cm wide
43. The biggest pound note you can get
44. 10% of 920 *(Hint, 10% is ¹⁄₁₀)*
47. The perimeter of a rectangle 50m long and 16m wide
49. £90 – £1.30 (give your answer in pounds)
51. What's the next number in the sequence 83, 88, 92, 95?
53. If x = 5 and y = 2, find 5x + 8y *(Hint, 5x would be 5 x 5)*
54. If the chance of Lenox Lewis losing his next fight is 28%, what's his chance of winning?

Clues down

3. The age you need to be to leave school in England.
5. Number of sides in 22 triangles
7. How many thirds make up 9 whole ones?
9. $3^2 + 5^2 + 6^2$
10. A triangle has angles 62° and 103°. What is the other angle?
11. 70 divided by the number of sides in a pentagon
12. The temperature in Alaska is –20°C, whilst the temperature in Brazil is 31°C. What is the difference in temperature?
13. $10^2 – 8$
15. (10 x 11) + 4
16. 22.57 accurate to 1 decimal place
18. Half a century + 5
23. 228 divided by 3 *(Hint, do 3s into 22 first and 'carry' the 1)*
25. A dozen
27. 1.4 x 1000 *(Hint, move the decimal place 3 places)*
29. 13.6 x 100 *(Hint, 24.6 x 100 = 2460)*
31. The chance of Michael Owen being injured for the next International is 42%. What's his chance of being fit?
32. Find x, if 2x + 1 = 93 *(Hint, do the opposite to + 1 first)*
33. Find the next term in the sequence 71, 75, 78, 80
37. (Triple 17) + 3
38. 58cm in metres *(Hint, it's 0. something)*
39. 0.03 + 0.04
40. 0.3 x 3 *(Hint, do 3 x 3 and put the point in)*
41. The square root of 121
42. 66 divided by 3 *(Hint, do 3s into 6 first)*
45. ⅓ of 87
48. The smallest number whose factors are 1, 2, 3 and 5
49. 9.0 – 0.9 *(Hint, do 90 – 9 and put the point in)*
50. 1.0 – 0.3 *(Hint, do 10 – 3 and put the point in)*
52. 10% of 700

How to Dazzle at Maths Crosswords Book 1

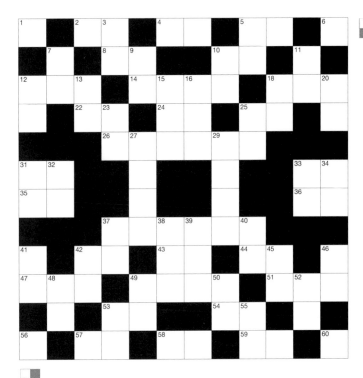

Crossword 1
Levels 5, 6 & 7

make sure you find all 11 decimal points

Clues across

1. The 4th prime number
2. The number of days in February – 7
4. Number of sides in a decagon
5. 1m – 38cm (give your answer in cm)
6. Simplify 3n + 4 – 2n – 2 – n
8. 8 squared + 2 + 1
10. 2 to the power 4 (Hint, 2 to the power 5 = 2 x 2 x 2 x 2 x 2)
12. 12.3 + 45.6 (Hint, do 123 + 456 and then put the point in)
14. ⅛ as a decimal (Hint, a quarter is 0.25, now halve this)
18. 109 x 5
22. The volume of a cube 3cm long (Hint, a cube 2cm long has a volume of 8cm)
24. 0.3 x 4 (Hint, do 3 x 4 then put the point in)
25. The coordinates (0,15), (1,16), (2,17), (3,18) all lie on the line y = x + ?
26. Write six hundred and fourteen thousand, six hundred and twelve in figures.
31. 53.6 to the nearest whole number
33. 1% of 8200
35. If 50% of something is 43, what's the total?
36. 72 ÷ (the number of sides in a quadrilateral)
37. Half a million
42. Area of a rectangle 6cm long and 4cm wide
43. A monkey ÷ 10 (A 'monkey' is slang for fifty tenners)
44. 10% of 920
47. The perimeter of a rectangle 50½m long and 15½m wide
49. £100 – £11.30
51. What's the next number in the sequence, 1075, 1050, 1025, 1000.
53. 50 + (–3 x 3)
54. If the chance of Lenox Lewis losing his next fight is 28%, what's his chance of winning it?
56. If 5f + 35 = 5(f + 7) then 4f + 24 = 4(f + ?)
57. 6 ÷ 10
58. ⅔ of 30 (Hint, find ⅓ first)
59. 3% of 400
60. If x = 3 and y = 2, find 7x – 10y

Clues down

3. The age you need to be to leave school in England
5. Number of sides in 22 triangles
7. How many thirds make up 9 whole ones?
9. The number of senses in the human body, e.g. smell x 14
10. A triangle has angles 62° and 103°. What is the other angle?
11. 70 divided by the number of sides in a pentagon
12. The temperature in Alaska is –20°C, whilst the temperature in Brazil is 31°C. What is the difference in temperature?
13. 10^2 – 8
15. (10 x 11) + 4
16. 22.57 accurate to 1 decimal place
18. Half a century + 5
20. The biggest pound note you can get
23. 228 divided by 3 (Hint, do 3s into 22 first)
25. A dozen
27. 1.4 x 1000 (Hint, move the decimal place)
29. 136,000 ÷ 100
31. The chance of David Seaman being dropped for the next International is 42%. What's his chance of being picked?
32. Find x, if 3(x + 4) = 150 (Hint, do the opposite to x 3 first)
33. Find the next term in the sequence 1, 3, 9, 27
34. 5^2 + 3
37. (Triple 17) + 3
38. 58cm in metres (A centimetre is 100 times smaller)
39. 0.03 + 0.04
40. 0.3 x 3
41. The square root of 121
42. 132 divided by 6 (Hint, do 6s into 13 first)
45. ⅓ of 87
46. The smallest number whose factors are 1, 3 and 5
48. The smallest number whose factors are 1, 2, 3 and 5
49. 9 – 0.9
50. 1 – 0.3
52. 10% of 700
53. 230 divided by the number of sides in a pentagon
55. (4 x 15) – (3 x 13)

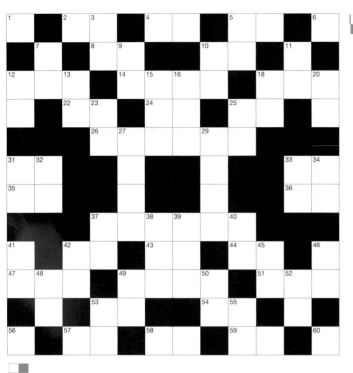

Crossword 1
Levels 6 & 7

make sure you find all 11 decimal points

Clues down
3. The age you need to be to leave school in England
5. Number of sides in 22 triangles
7. In a survey 3 out of 40 people's favourite wrestler was 'Rakishi'. What angle would be shaded on a pie chart? *(Hint, find the angle that is the whole pie ÷ 40 first)*
9. The number of senses the body has, eg smell x 14
10. An isosceles triangle has one angle measuring 150°. State the size of one of the others.
11. If x = 2 and y = −2, find $x^2 − 5y$ *(Be careful with the 'minuses')*
12. The temperature in Alaska is −20.2°C, whilst the temperature in Brazil is 30.8°C. What is the difference in temperature?
13. (12 x 13) − 64
15. (14 x 14) − 82
16. 22.57 accurate to 1 decimal place
18. Half a century + 5
20. A bull's eye
23. 456 divided by 6
25. A dozen
27. 0.0014×10^6 *(Hint, move the decimal point)*
29. 1360000×10^{-3}
31. The chance of David Seaman being dropped for the next International is 42%. What's his chance of being picked?
32. Find x, if 3(x + 4) = 150
33. If the nth term of a sequence is 4n+1, what is the 20th term?
34. √225 + 13
37. 1/6 = 9/?
38. 580mm in metres
39. If $^6/_{10} \times ^7/_{10} = 0.42$ then $^1/_{10} \times ^7/_{10} = ?$ (as a decimal)
40. On a 10 sided spinner, what's the probability of not spinning a 10? (as a decimal)
41. The square root of 121
42. 264 divided by 12 *(Hint, do 12s into 26 first)*
45. ⅛ of 232
46. The smallest number whose factors are 1, 3 and 5
48. The smallest number whose factors are 1, 2, 3 and 5
49. 9 − 0.9
50. On a 10 sided spinner, the chance of getting more than a 3, as a decimal *(It's numbered 1 to 10)*
52. 10% of 700
53. 230 divided by the number of sides on a pentagon
55. Area of a triangle with base 1½cm and vertical height 28cm

Clues across
1. The 4th prime number
2. The number of days in February − 7
4. Number of sides in a decagon
5. 620mm in cm
6. Simplify $n^2 + 3n + 4 − 2n − n^2 − 2 − n$
8. 8 squared + 2 squared − 1 squared
10. $(x + 4)(x + 4) = x^2 + 8x + ?$
12. 12.3 + 45.6
14. ⅛ as a decimal *(Hint, a quarter is 0.25)*
18. 10.9 x 50 *(Hint, think of 50 as 10 x 5)*
22. The volume of a cube 3cm long
24. 0.3 x 0.4 x 10
25. The coordinates (−2, 13), (−1,14), (0,15), (1,16) all lie on the line y = x + ?
26. 6.14612×10^5
31. 53.6 to 2 significant figures
33. 1% of 8,200
35. If 25% of something is 21.5, what's the total?
36. 1/2 + 4/9 = 17/? *(Hint, change both fractions so they have a common denominator)*
37. Half a million
42. Area of a rectangle 96cm long and ¼cm wide
43. A monkey ÷ 10 *(Hint, a monkey is slang for 50 tenners)*
44. ½% of 18,400
47. The perimeter of a rectangle 50.1m long and 15.9m wide
49. 90 pounds − 130 pence (give your answer in pounds)
51. What's the next number in the sequence, 1135, 1080, 1035, 1000
53. (−5 x −10) + (−3 x 3)
54. If the chance of Lenox Lewis losing his next fight is 28%, what's his chance of winning it?
56. The ratio 30:18 is the same as 10:?
57. 6 ÷ 10
58. 4/5 + 4/20 = ?/20 *(Hint, change 4/5 into twentieths)*
59. ⅓% of 3600 *(Hint, find 1% first)*
60. $9f^2g − 3fg$ when factorised = 3fg(3f − ?)

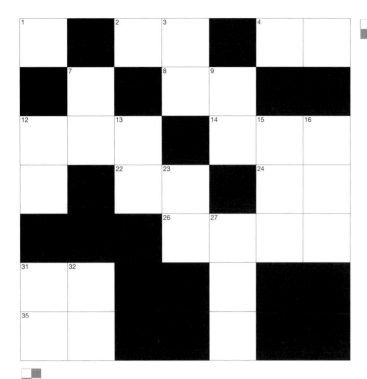

Crossword 2
Level 1

make sure you find all 4 decimal points

Clues across

1. How many 'Musketeers' were there?
2. (3 x 3) + 2
4. (Half of 10) + 19
8. (6 shared between 3) + 17
12. 400 + 300
14. Is 432 closer to a) 430 or b) 440?
22. 59 – (2 x 2)
24. (50% or a half of £10) + £33
26. Is four thousand and seventy-six a) 4076 or b) 4760?
31. 70💣 + 20💣 = ?💣
35. (A quarter of 8) + 73 *(Hint, to find a ¼, you halve it then halve it again)*

Clues down

3. 1 + 2 + 3 + 4 + ½ + ½
7. Number of wheels on 15 motor bikes
9. What's next in this sequence? 86, 88, 90, 92
12. 50 + (2 x 5) + (5 x 2)
13. Is 1.7 – 1.2, a) 0.5, b) 0.6, or c) 0.7?
15. Is 336.9 closer to a) 336 or b) 337?
16. What's the biggest amount of money? a) £0.74, b) £0.69, or c) £0.86
23. ? + 4 = 58
27. If one chew costs £0.11, what do two cost? Is it a) £0.22, b) £1.11, or c) £0.13?
31. 101 – 4
32. Is a ½ also known as a) 0.4, b) 0.5, or c) 0.6?

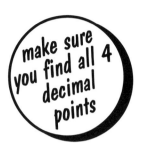

Crossword 2 Levels 1 & 2

make sure you find all 4 decimal points

Clues across

1. How many 'Musketeers' were there?
2. (2 x 3) + 10 – 5
4. (Half of 10) + 19
8. (9 shared between 3) + 16
12. 600 + 80 + 10 + 10
14. Is 432 closer to a) 430 or b) 440?
22. 54 – (2 x 2) + 5
24. (50% of £10) + £33 *(Remember, 50% is the same as a half)*
26. Write four thousand and seventy-six in figures
31. 70✝ + 20✝ = ?✝
35. (A quarter of 8) + 73

Clues down

3. 1 + 2 + 3 + 4 + ½ + ½
7. ½ + 24 + ½ + 2 + 3
9. What's next in this sequence? 86, 88, 90, 92
12. 50 + (2 x 5) + (5 x 2)
13. 3.7 – 3.2 *(Hint, it's like 37 – 32)*
15. Is 336.9 to the nearest whole one a) 336 or b) 337?
16. If the chance of you getting a grade B in your GCSE is 0.14, what is the chance of you not getting a B? Is it a) 0.96 or b) 0.86?
23. ? + 4 = 58
27. If one chew costs £0.11, what do two cost? Is it a) £0.22, b) £1.11, or c) £0.13?
31. 106 – 9
32. If one bed bug measures 0.1cm, what do 5 of them measure?

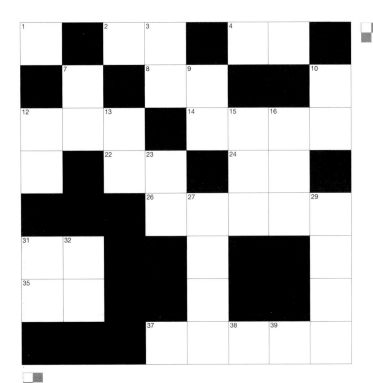

Crossword 2
Levels 2 & 3

make sure you find all 6 decimal points

Clues across
1. How many 'Musketeers' were there?
2. (6 x 3) + 10 – 17
4. If 1% of £600 is £6, what is 4% of £600?
8. (Half of 16) + 11
12. Find 50% of £200. Now add £600.
14. Is 4321 closer to a) 4300 or b) 4400?
22. 64 – 3² *(Hint, 4² means 4 x 4)*
24. (25% of £8) + £36
26. Write in figures, forty thousand-seven hundred and sixty
31. 60℗ + 20℗ + 10℗ = ?℗
35. (½ of 100) + 25
37. Which number is bigger? a) 3456.6 or b) 3456.7

Clues down
3. 22 ÷ 2
7. ½ + 24 + ½ + 2 + 3
9. 10cm – 6mm (give the answer in mm). Is it a) 40mm, b) 96mm, or c) 94mm?
10. (The number of days in a week) times this by 10
12. (5 x 6) + (4 x 5) + (5 x 4)
13. 3.7 – 3.2 *(Hint, it's like 37 – 32)*
15. 336.9 to the nearest whole one
16. If the chance of you getting a grade B in your GCSE is 0.14, what is the chance of you not getting a B? Is it a) 0.96 or b) 0.86?
23. Triple 18
27. 0.112 x 2. Is it a) 0.222, b) 0.114, or c) 0.224?
29. What's next in this sequence? 0.015, 0.013, 0.011, 0.009
31. A pack of pencils costing £1.17 had 20p off. Is the new price in pence a) 98p, b) 87p, or c) 97p?
32. If 0.2 + 0.2 + 0.4 = 0.8, then 0.2 + 0.2 + 0.1 = ?

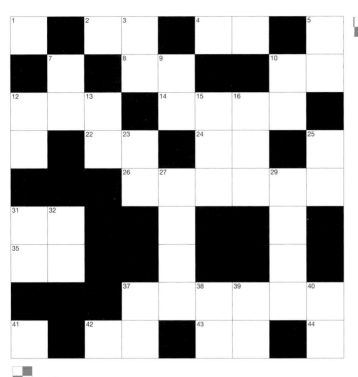

Crossword 2
Levels 2, 3 & 4

make sure you find all 6 decimal points

Clues across

1. How many 'Musketeers' were there?
2. Which of these numbers has the fewest factors? a) 11, b) 12, or c) 15 *(Hint, 6 has four factors, 1, 2, 3 and 6)*
4. If 1% of £600 is £6, what is 4% of £600?
8. What number times itself makes 16? Now add 15 to this.
10. $36 + 42$
12. Find 50% of £300. Now add £550.
14. 4321 to the nearest 100. Is it a) 4000, b) 4300, or c) 4400?
22. $64 - 3^2$ *(Hint, 4^2 means 4 x 4)*
24. If $x = 10$, find $3x + 8$
26. Four hundred and seven thousand-six hundred and four
31. 100ⵔ $+ 30$ⵔ $- 40$ⵔ $= ?$ⵔ
35. (¼ of 100) + 50
37. Is 3456.789 closer to a) 3456.78 or b) 3456.79?
42. Josh was gutted when he realised there were 3 times as many boys as girls at his party. If there were 6 girls, how many boys were there?
43. $(3 \times 7) + (3 \times 10) + 29$

Clues down

3. $22 \div 2$
5. $? - 6 = 22$
7. $½ + 24 + ½ + 2 + ½ + 2 + ½$
9. 10cm – 6mm (give the answer in mm)
10. (Days in a week) times this by 10
12. $? \div 7 = 10$ *(Hint, it's 10 times as big as)*
13. $3.7 - 3.2$ *(Hint, it's like 37 – 32)*
15. 336.9 to the nearest whole one
16. If the chance of you getting a grade B in your GCSE is 0.14, what is the chance of you not getting a B? Is it a) 0.14, b) 0.50, or c) 0.86?
23. Triple 18
25. $(14 \div 2) + (21 \div 3)$
27. 0.112×2 *(Hint, it's like 112 x 2)*
29. What's next in this sequence? 0.015, 0.013, 0.011, 0.009
31. A pack of pencils costing £1.17 had 20p off. Write its new price in pence.
32. $0.2 + 0.2 + 0.1$ *(Hint, it's like 2 + 2 + 1)*
37. $(7 \times 11) - 40 + 1$
38. 5.8×10
39. $600 \div 10$ *(Hint, $900 \div 10 = 90$)*
40. $98 - 2^2$
41. Five bed bugs measure 10mm. What does one of them measure?

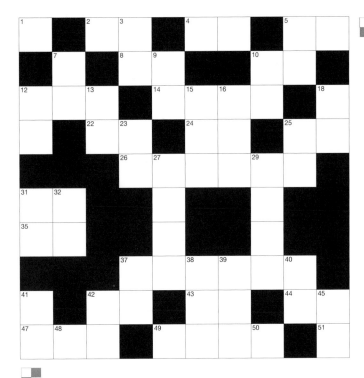

Crossword 2
Levels 3, 4 & 5

make sure you find all 8 decimal points

Clues across

1. In any of these coordinates (0,3), (1,4), (2,5), (3,6), what do you always add to the x part to get the y part? *(Hint, the x part is the 1st number and the y part is the 2nd)*
2. The next prime number after 7 *(Hint, it has 2 factors, 1 and itself)*
4. If 1% of £600 is £6, what is 4% of £600?
5. $3^2 + 4^2$ *(Hint, 6^2 means 6 x 6)*
8. What number times itself makes 25? Now add 14 to this.
10. 36 + 42
12. 1% of £70,000 *(Hint, you can find 1% by knocking of some zeros)*
14. 4321 to the nearest 100. Is it a) 4000 b) 4300 or c) 4400?
22. $64 - 3^2$
24. If x = 6, find 6x + 2
25. $22f - 10f - 1f = ?f$
26. Write four hundred and seven thousand, six hundred and four, in figures
31. Without your calculator, estimate 10.1 x 8.91. Is it a) 60, b) 80, or c) 90?
35. ¾ of 100 *(Hint, find ¼ first)*
37. Is 3456.789 closer to a) 3456.78 or b) 3456.79?
42. Josh was gutted when he realised the ratio of boys to girls at his party was 3:1. There were 6 girls who turned up. How many boys were there? *(Hint, 3:1 means 3 boys to every 1 girl)*
43. (3 x 7) + (3 x 9) + 32
44. 100 + 200 – 300 + 40
47. How many pairs of boots are worn by the centipede basketball team? *(Hint, there are 5 in a team)*
49. 2002 – ½ – ¼ – ½ – ¼ – ¼ – ¼

Clues down

3. 22 ÷ 2
5. Find x, if x – 26 = 2
7. What's next in this sequence? 44, 39, 35, 32 *(Hint, it's not 29)*
9. 10cm – 6mm (give the answer in mm)
10. (The number of days in a week) times this by 10
12. Find x, if x/7 = 10 *(Hint, what's 7 times as big as 10?)*
13. 3.7 – 3.2 *(Hint, it's like 37 – 32)*
15. 336.9 to the nearest whole one
16. If the chance of you getting a grade B in your GCSE is 0.14, what is the chance of you not getting a B? Is it a) 0.14, b) 0.50, or c) 0.86?
18. $6^2 + 2^2 + 1^2$ *(Hint, 1^2 is not 2)*
23. Triple 18
25. (14 ÷ 2) + (21 ÷ 3)
27. 0.112 x 2 *(Hint, it's like 112 x 2)*
29. What's next in this sequence? 0.015, 0.013, 0.011, 0.009
31. A pack of pencils costing £1.17 had 20p off. Write its new price in pence.
32. 5.8 – 5.3 *(Hint, it's zero point something)*
37. (7 x 11) – 40 + 1
38. 58 x 10
39. 6000 ÷ 10
40. $98 - 2^2$
41. Two bed bugs measure 4.4mm. What does one of them measure?
42. 5/10 + 1/10 = 6/?
45. Half of 0.2

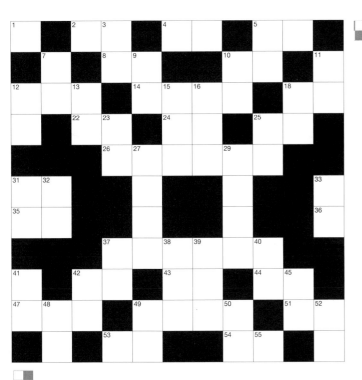

Crossword 1 Levels 4, 5 & 6

make sure you find all 10 decimal points

Clues across

1. The 4th prime number *(Hint, the 1st is 2)*
2. The number of days in February – 7
4. (Number of sides in a pentagon) x 2
5. 1m – 38cm (give your answer in cm)
8. 8 squared + 2 + 1
10. 2 x 2 x 2 x 2
12. 12.3 + 45.6 *(Hint, do 123 + 456 and then put the point in)*
14. ½ of 0.25 *(Hint, do ½ of 25 and then move the point)*
18. (10 x 5) + √16
22. The volume of a cube 3cm long, 3cm wide and 3cm high
24. 0.3 x 4 *(Hint, do 3 x 4 then put the point in)*
25. The coordinates (0,15), (1,16), (2,17), (3,18) all lie on the line y = x + ? *(Hint, what do you always add to the x part to get the y part of the coordinate?)*
26. Write six hundred and fourteen thousand, six hundred and twelve in figures
31. 53.6 to the nearest whole number
33. 1% of 800
35. If 50% of something is 43, what's the total?
36. 4 ÷ (the number of sides in a quadrilateral)
37. Half a million
42. Area of a rectangle 6cm long and 4cm wide
43. The biggest pound note you can get
44. 10% of 920 *(Hint, 10% is ¹⁄₁₀)*
47. The perimeter of a rectangle 50m long and 16m wide
49. £90 – £1.30 (give your answer in pounds)
51. What's the next number in the sequence 83, 88, 92, 95?
53. If x = 5 and y = 2, find 5x + 8y *(Hint, 5x would be 5 x 5)*
54. If the chance of Lenox Lewis losing his next fight is 28%, what's his chance of winning?

Clues down

3. The age you need to be to leave school in England.
5. Number of sides in 22 triangles
7. How many thirds make up 9 whole ones?
9. $3^2 + 5^2 + 6^2$
10. A triangle has angles 62° and 103°. What is the other angle?
11. 70 divided by the number of sides in a pentagon
12. The temperature in Alaska is –20°C, whilst the temperature in Brazil is 31°C. What is the difference in temperature?
13. $10^2 – 8$
15. (10 x 11) + 4
16. 22.57 accurate to 1 decimal place
18. Half a century + 5
23. 228 divided by 3 *(Hint, do 3s into 22 first and 'carry' the 1)*
25. A dozen
27. 1.4 x 1000 *(Hint, move the decimal place 3 places)*
29. 13.6 x 100 *(Hint, 24.6 x 100 = 2460)*
31. The chance of Michael Owen being injured for the next International is 42%. What's his chance of being fit?
32. Find x, if 2x + 1 = 93 *(Hint, do the opposite to + 1 first)*
33. Find the next term in the sequence 71, 75, 78, 80
37. (Triple 17) + 3
38. 58cm in metres *(Hint, it's 0. something)*
39. 0.03 + 0.04
40. 0.3 x 3 *(Hint, do 3 x 3 and put the point in)*
41. The square root of 121
42. 66 divided by 3 *(Hint, do 3s into 6 first)*
45. ⅓ of 87
48. The smallest number whose factors are 1, 2, 3 and 5
49. 9.0 – 0.9 *(Hint, do 90 – 9 and put the point in)*
50. 1.0 – 0.3 *(Hint, do 10 – 3 and put the point in)*
52. 10% of 700

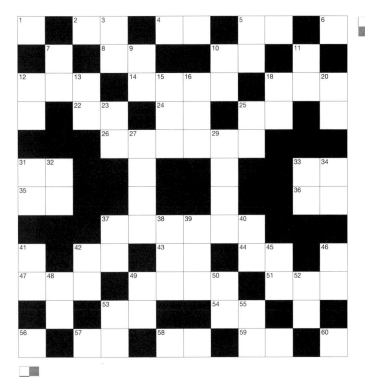

Crossword 1
Levels 5, 6 & 7

make sure you find all 11 decimal points

Clues across
1. The 4th prime number
2. The number of days in February – 7
4. Number of sides in a decagon
5. 1m – 38cm (give your answer in cm)
6. Simplify 3n + 4 – 2n – 2 – n
8. 8 squared + 2 + 1
10. 2 to the power 4 (Hint, 2 to the power 5 = 2 x 2 x 2 x 2 x 2)
12. 12.3 + 45.6 (Hint, do 123 + 456 and then put the point in)
14. ⅛ as a decimal (Hint, a quarter is 0.25, now halve this)
18. 109 x 5
22. The volume of a cube 3cm long (Hint, a cube 2cm long has a volume of 8cm)
24. 0.3 x 4 (Hint, do 3 x 4 then put the point in)
25. The coordinates (0,15), (1,16), (2,17), (3,18) all lie on the line y = x + ?
26. Write six hundred and fourteen thousand, six hundred and twelve in figures.
31. 53.6 to the nearest whole number
33. 1% of 8200
35. If 50% of something is 43, what's the total?
36. 72 ÷ (the number of sides in a quadrilateral)
37. Half a million
42. Area of a rectangle 6cm long and 4cm wide
43. A monkey ÷ 10 (A 'monkey' is slang for fifty tenners)
44. 10% of 920
47. The perimeter of a rectangle 50½m long and 15½m wide
49. £100 – £11.30
51. What's the next number in the sequence, 1075, 1050, 1025, 1000.
53. 50 + (–3 x 3)
54. If the chance of Lenox Lewis losing his next fight is 28%, what's his chance of winning it?
56. If 5f + 35 = 5(f + 7) then 4f + 24 = 4(f + ?)
57. 6 ÷ 10
58. ⅔ of 30 (Hint, find ⅓ first)
59. 3% of 400
60. If x = 3 and y = 2, find 7x – 10y

Clues down
3. The age you need to be to leave school in England
5. Number of sides in 22 triangles
7. How many thirds make up 9 whole ones?
9. The number of senses in the human body, e.g. smell x 14
10. A triangle has angles 62° and 103°. What is the other angle?
11. 70 divided by the number of sides in a pentagon
12. The temperature in Alaska is –20°C, whilst the temperature in Brazil is 31°C. What is the difference in temperature?
13. $10^2 – 8$
15. (10 x 11) + 4
16. 22.57 accurate to 1 decimal place
18. Half a century + 5
20. The biggest pound note you can get
23. 228 divided by 3 (Hint, do 3s into 22 first)
25. A dozen
27. 1.4 x 1000 (Hint, move the decimal place)
29. 136,000 ÷ 100
31. The chance of David Seaman being dropped for the next International is 42%. What's his chance of being picked?
32. Find x, if 3(x + 4) = 150 (Hint, do the opposite to x 3 first)
33. Find the next term in the sequence 1, 3, 9, 27
34. $5^2 + 3$
37. (Triple 17) + 3
38. 58cm in metres (A centimetre is 100 times smaller)
39. 0.03 + 0.04
40. 0.3 x 3
41. The square root of 121
42. 132 divided by 6 (Hint, do 6s into 13 first)
45. ⅓ of 87
46. The smallest number whose factors are 1, 3 and 5
48. The smallest number whose factors are 1, 2, 3 and 5
49. 9 – 0.9
50. 1 – 0.3
52. 10% of 700
53. 230 divided by the number of sides in a pentagon
55. (4 x 15) – (3 x 13)

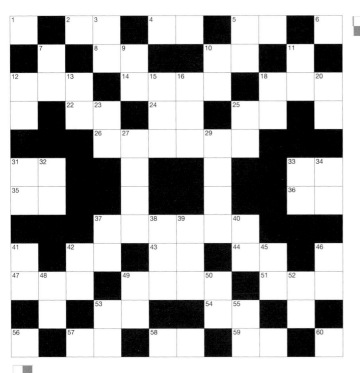

make sure you find all 11 decimal points

Clues down

3. The age you need to be to leave school in England
5. Number of sides in 22 triangles
7. In a survey 3 out of 40 people's favourite wrestler was 'Rakishi'. What angle would be shaded on a pie chart? *(Hint, find the angle that is the whole pie ÷ 40 first)*
9. The number of senses the body has, eg smell x 14
10. An isosceles triangle has one angle measuring 150°. State the size of one of the others.
11. If $x = 2$ and $y = -2$, find $x^2 - 5y$ *(Be careful with the 'minuses')*
12. The temperature in Alaska is $-20.2°C$, whilst the temperature in Brazil is $30.8°C$. What is the difference in temperature?
13. $(12 \times 13) - 64$
15. $(14 \times 14) - 82$
16. 22.57 accurate to 1 decimal place
18. Half a century + 5
20. A bull's eye
23. 456 divided by 6
25. A dozen
27. 0.0014×10^6 *(Hint, move the decimal point)*
29. 1360000×10^{-3}
31. The chance of David Seaman being dropped for the next International is 42%. What's his chance of being picked?
32. Find x, if $3(x + 4) = 150$
33. If the nth term of a sequence is $4n+1$, what is the 20th term?
34. $\sqrt{225} + 13$
37. $1/6 = 9/?$
38. 580mm in metres
39. If $^6/_{10} \times ^7/_{10} = 0.42$ then $^1/_{10} \times ^7/_{10} = ?$ (as a decimal)
40. On a 10 sided spinner, what's the probability of not spinning a 10? (as a decimal)
41. The square root of 121
42. 264 divided by 12 *(Hint, do 12s into 26 first)*
45. $^1/_8$ of 232
46. The smallest number whose factors are 1, 3 and 5
48. The smallest number whose factors are 1, 2, 3 and 5
49. $9 - 0.9$
50. On a 10 sided spinner, the chance of getting more than a 3, as a decimal *(It's numbered 1 to 10)*
52. 10% of 700
53. 230 divided by the number of sides on a pentagon
55. Area of a triangle with base 1½cm and vertical height 28cm

Clues across

1. The 4th prime number
2. The number of days in February – 7
4. Number of sides in a decagon
5. 620mm in cm
6. Simplify $n^2 + 3n + 4 - 2n - n^2 - 2 - n$
8. 8 squared + 2 squared – 1 squared
10. $(x + 4)(x + 4) = x^2 + 8x + ?$
12. $12.3 + 45.6$
14. $^1/_8$ as a decimal *(Hint, a quarter is 0.25)*
18. 10.9×50 *(Hint, think of 50 as 10 x 5)*
22. The volume of a cube 3cm long
24. $0.3 \times 0.4 \times 10$
25. The coordinates $(-2, 13)$, $(-1,14)$, $(0,15)$, $(1,16)$ all lie on the line $y = x + ?$
26. 6.14612×10^5
31. 53.6 to 2 significant figures
33. 1% of 8,200
35. If 25% of something is 21.5, what's the total?
36. $1/2 + 4/9 = 17/?$ *(Hint, change both fractions so they have a common denominator)*
37. Half a million
42. Area of a rectangle 96cm long and ¼cm wide
43. A monkey ÷ 10 *(Hint, a monkey is slang for 50 tenners)*
44. ½% of 18,400
47. The perimeter of a rectangle 50.1m long and 15.9m wide
49. 90 pounds – 130 pence (give your answer in pounds)
51. What's the next number in the sequence, 1135, 1080, 1035, 1000
53. $(-5 \times -10) + (-3 \times 3)$
54. If the chance of Lenox Lewis losing his next fight is 28%, what's his chance of winning it?
56. The ratio 30:18 is the same as 10:?
57. $6 \div 10$
58. $4/5 + 4/20 = ?/20$ *(Hint, change 4/5 into twentieths)*
59. $^1/_3$% of 3600 *(Hint, find 1% first)*
60. $9f^2g - 3fg$ when factorised $= 3fg(3f - ?)$

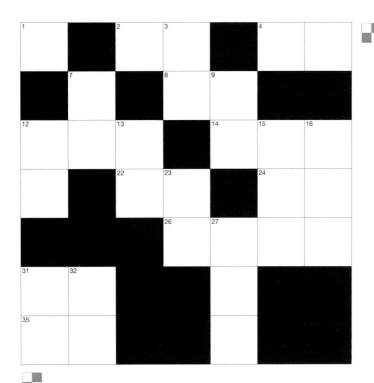

Crossword 2
Level 1

make sure you find all 4 decimal points

Clues across

1. How many 'Musketeers' were there?
2. (3 x 3) + 2
4. (Half of 10) + 19
8. (6 shared between 3) + 17
12. 400 + 300
14. Is 432 closer to a) 430 or b) 440?
22. 59 − (2 x 2)
24. (50% or a half of £10) + £33
26. Is four thousand and seventy-six a) 4076 or b) 4760?
31. 70💣 + 20💣 = ?💣
35. (A quarter of 8) + 73 *(Hint, to find a ¼, you halve it then halve it again)*

Clues down

3. 1 + 2 + 3 + 4 + ½ + ½
7. Number of wheels on 15 motor bikes
9. What's next in this sequence? 86, 88, 90, 92
12. 50 + (2 x 5) + (5 x 2)
13. Is 1.7 − 1.2, a) 0.5, b) 0.6, or c) 0.7?
15. Is 336.9 closer to a) 336 or b) 337?
16. What's the biggest amount of money? a) £0.74, b) £0.69, or c) £0.86
23. ? + 4 = 58
27. If one chew costs £0.11, what do two cost? Is it a) £0.22, b) £1.11, or c) £0.13?
31. 101 − 4
32. Is a ½ also known as a) 0.4, b) 0.5, or c) 0.6?

Crossword 2
Levels 1 & 2

make sure you find all 4 decimal points

Clues across

1. How many 'Musketeers' were there?
2. (2 x 3) + 10 – 5
4. (Half of 10) + 19
8. (9 shared between 3) + 16
12. 600 + 80 + 10 + 10
14. Is 432 closer to a) 430 or b) 440?
22. 54 – (2 x 2) + 5
24. (50% of £10) + £33 (Remember, 50% is the same as a half)
26. Write four thousand and seventy-six in figures
31. 70✝ + 20✝ = ?✝
35. (A quarter of 8) + 73

Clues down

3. 1 + 2 + 3 + 4 + ½ + ½
7. ½ + 24 + ½ + 2 + 3
9. What's next in this sequence? 86, 88, 90, 92
12. 50 + (2 x 5) + (5 x 2)
13. 3.7 – 3.2 (Hint, it's like 37 – 32)
15. Is 336.9 to the nearest whole one a) 336 or b) 337?
16. If the chance of you getting a grade B in your GCSE is 0.14, what is the chance of you not getting a B? Is it a) 0.96 or b) 0.86?
23. ? + 4 = 58
27. If one chew costs £0.11, what do two cost? Is it a) £0.22, b) £1.11, or c) £0.13?
31. 106 – 9
32. If one bed bug measures 0.1cm, what do 5 of them measure?

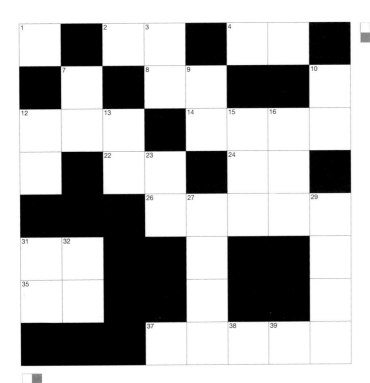

make sure you find all 6 decimal points

Clues across

1. How many 'Musketeers' were there?
2. (6 x 3) + 10 − 17
4. If 1% of £600 is £6, what is 4% of £600?
8. (Half of 16) + 11
12. Find 50% of £200. Now add £600.
14. Is 4321 closer to a) 4300 or b) 4400?
22. $64 - 3^2$ (Hint, 4^2 means 4 x 4)
24. (25% of £8) + £36
26. Write in figures, forty thousand-seven hundred and sixty
31. $60 \square + 20 \square + 10 \square = ? \square$
35. (½ of 100) + 25
37. Which number is bigger? a) 3456.6 or b) 3456.7

Clues down

3. 22 ÷ 2
7. ½ + 24 + ½ + 2 + 3
9. 10cm − 6mm (give the answer in mm). Is it a) 40mm, b) 96mm, or c) 94mm?
10. (The number of days in a week) times this by 10
12. (5 x 6) + (4 x 5) + (5 x 4)
13. 3.7 − 3.2 (Hint, it's like 37 − 32)
15. 336.9 to the nearest whole one
16. If the chance of you getting a grade B in your GCSE is 0.14, what is the chance of you not getting a B? Is it a) 0.96 or b) 0.86?
23. Triple 18
27. 0.112 x 2. Is it a) 0.222, b) 0.114, or c) 0.224?
29. What's next in this sequence? 0.015, 0.013, 0.011, 0.009
31. A pack of pencils costing £1.17 had 20p off. Is the new price in pence a) 98p, b) 87p, or c) 97p?
32. If 0.2 + 0.2 + 0.4 = 0.8, then 0.2 + 0.2 + 0.1 = ?

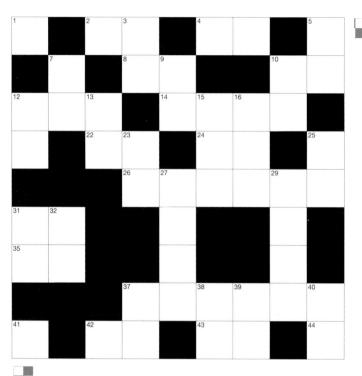

make sure you find all 6 decimal points

Clues across

1. How many 'Musketeers' were there?
2. Which of these numbers has the fewest factors? a) 11, b) 12, or c) 15 *(Hint, 6 has four factors, 1, 2, 3 and 6)*
4. If 1% of £600 is £6, what is 4% of £600?
8. What number times itself makes 16? Now add 15 to this.
10. 36 + 42
12. Find 50% of £300. Now add £550.
14. 4321 to the nearest 100. Is it a) 4000, b) 4300, or c) 4400?
22. $64 - 3^2$ *(Hint, 4^2 means 4 x 4)*
24. If x = 10, find 3x + 8
26. Four hundred and seven thousand-six hundred and four
31. $100฿ + 30฿ - 40฿ = ?฿$
35. (¼ of 100) + 50
37. Is 3456.789 closer to a) 3456.78 or b) 3456.79?
42. Josh was gutted when he realised there were 3 times as many boys as girls at his party. If there were 6 girls, how many boys were there?
43. (3 x 7) + (3 x 10) + 29

Clues down

3. $22 \div 2$
5. ? − 6 = 22
7. ½ + 24 + ½ + 2 + ½ + 2 + ½
9. 10cm − 6mm (give the answer in mm)
10. (Days in a week) times this by 10
12. ? ÷ 7 = 10 *(Hint, it's 10 times as big as)*
13. 3.7 − 3.2 *(Hint, it's like 37 − 32)*
15. 336.9 to the nearest whole one
16. If the chance of you getting a grade B in your GCSE is 0.14, what is the chance of you not getting a B? Is it a) 0.14, b) 0.50, or c) 0.86?
23. Triple 18
25. (14 ÷ 2) + (21 ÷ 3)
27. 0.112 x 2 *(Hint, it's like 112 x 2)*
29. What's next in this sequence? 0.015, 0.013, 0.011, 0.009
31. A pack of pencils costing £1.17 had 20p off. Write its new price in pence.
32. 0.2 + 0.2 + 0.1 *(Hint, it's like 2 + 2 + 1)*
37. (7 x 11) − 40 + 1
38. 5.8 x 10
39. 600 ÷ 10 *(Hint, 900 ÷ 10 = 90)*
40. $98 - 2^2$
41. Five bed bugs measure 10mm. What does one of them measure?

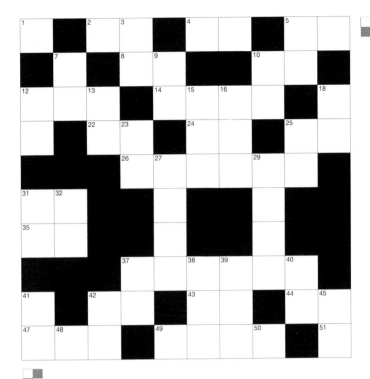

Crossword 2
Levels 3, 4 & 5

make sure you find all 8 decimal points

Clues across

1. In any of these coordinates (0,3), (1,4), (2,5), (3,6), what do you always add to the x part to get the y part? *(Hint, the x part is the 1st number and the y part is the 2nd)*
2. The next prime number after 7 *(Hint, it has 2 factors, 1 and itself)*
4. If 1% of £600 is £6, what is 4% of £600?
5. $3^2 + 4^2$ *(Hint, 6^2 means 6 x 6)*
8. What number times itself makes 25? Now add 14 to this.
10. 36 + 42
12. 1% of £70,000 *(Hint, you can find 1% by knocking of some zeros)*
14. 4321 to the nearest 100. Is it a) 4000 b) 4300 or c) 4400?
22. $64 - 3^2$
24. If x = 6, find 6x + 2
25. 22£ – 10£ – 1£ = ?£
26. Write four hundred and seven thousand, six hundred and four, in figures
31. Without your calculator, estimate 10.1 x 8.91. Is it a) 60, b) 80, or c) 90?
35. ¾ of 100 *(Hint, find ¼ first)*
37. Is 3456.789 closer to a) 3456.78 or b) 3456.79?
42. Josh was gutted when he realised the ratio of boys to girls at his party was 3:1. There were 6 girls who turned up. How many boys were there? *(Hint, 3:1 means 3 boys to every 1 girl)*
43. (3 x 7) + (3 x 9) + 32
44. 100 + 200 – 300 + 40
47. How many pairs of boots are worn by the centipede basketball team? *(Hint, there are 5 in a team)*
49. 2002 – ½ – ¼ – ½ – ¼ – ¼ – ¼

Clues down

3. 22 ÷ 2
5. Find x, if x – 26 = 2
7. What's next in this sequence? 44, 39, 35, 32 *(Hint, it's not 29)*
9. 10cm – 6mm (give the answer in mm)
10. (The number of days in a week) times this by 10
12. Find x, if x/7 = 10 *(Hint, what's 7 times as big as 10?)*
13. 3.7 – 3.2 *(Hint, it's like 37 – 32)*
15. 336.9 to the nearest whole one
16. If the chance of you getting a grade B in your GCSE is 0.14, what is the chance of you not getting a B? Is it a) 0.14, b) 0.50, or c) 0.86?
18. $6^2 + 2^2 + 1^2$ *(Hint, 1^2 is not 2)*
23. Triple 18
25. (14 ÷ 2) + (21 ÷ 3)
27. 0.112 x 2 *(Hint, it's like 112 x 2)*
29. What's next in this sequence? 0.015, 0.013, 0.011, 0.009
31. A pack of pencils costing £1.17 had 20p off. Write its new price in pence.
32. 5.8 – 5.3 *(Hint, it's zero point something)*
37. (7 x 11) – 40 + 1
38. 58 x 10
39. 6000 ÷ 10
40. $98 - 2^2$
41. Two bed bugs measure 4.4mm. What does one of them measure?
42. 5/10 + 1/10 = 6/?
45. Half of 0.2

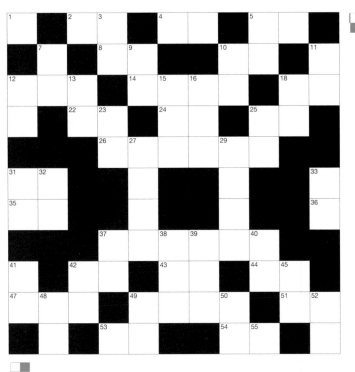

Crossword 4
Levels 4, 5 & 6

make sure you find all 8 decimal points

Clues across

1. 5.8 to the nearest whole number
2. The 5th prime number *(Hint, the first is 2)*
4. 7% of £300 *(Hint, find 1% first)*
5. If the ratio of boys to girls in the class is 9:12 how many boys will there be if there are 24 girls in the class? *(Hint, see how many 12s are in 24 first, then 2 lots of 12 make 24)*
8. 6 squared + 2
10. $2(8f - 5) = ?f - 10$
12. A pair of gloves cost £8.96 originally. How much are they with 25% off?
14. 1269 to the nearest hundred
18. Is 2.98 + 2.04 closer to a) 5.0 or b) 5.1? *(Hint, do 298 + 204 first)*
22. The mean of 14, 16, 11 and 11 *(Add them all and ÷ by 4)*
24. If 3700g = 3.7kg, what is 2400g in kg?
25. 50% of 144
26. Write three hundred and thirteen thousand, six hundred and twelve in figures
31. 70 out of 100 as a %
35. Area of a square with side length 5cm
37. 4567.679 to 2 decimal places
42. The perimeter of a square whose side length is 8cm *(Perimeter = length around outside)*
43. If 3q x 2 = 6q, then 2q x 5 = ?q
44. Find x, if $x - 21 = -2$
47. If 8.73 x 100 = 873, then what is 4.56 x 100?
49. 6000 – 110
51. Gorgeous ice cream with cone and flake
53. The area in cm² of a square whose length is 7cm
54. Angles in a triangle ÷ 10

Clues down

3. 12.9 to the nearest whole number
5. Simplify $7x - 4 - 3x + 20 - 4x$
7. What's the legal age to drive in England?
9. 9 squared
10. Cedric the centipede put on 45 pairs of bed socks to keep himself warm. How many of his feet were left uncovered?
11. What is the median of 23, 21, 16, 12, 25, 24, 17, 17, 20? *(Hint, put them in order first, then find the middle one)*
12. 248 divided by 4 *(Hint, do 4s into 24 first)*
13. What is $^{21}/_{100}$ as a %? *(Hint, $^{23}/_{100} = 23\%$)*
15. (10 x 31) + 13
16. If the chance of Zainah being late for registration at least once this week is 0.54, what's the chance that she won't be?
18. 64/100 – 12/100 = ?/100
23. 198 divided by 6 *(Hint, do 6s into 19 first, then carry the 1)*
25. 25% of 288
27. 1.345 x 1000 *(Hint, 2.345 x 1000 = 2345)*
29. 11.56 x 100
31. 1m – 28cm (give the answer in cm)
32. $^{50}/_{100}$ as a decimal *(Hint, $^{40}/_{100} = 0.4$)*
33. (75% of £40) + £35
37. 12 + (⅓ of 90)
38. 316 + 302
39. $(7 \times 100) + 3^2$
40. What is the next number in the sequence? 1, 3, 9, 27
41. If a circle has a radius of 37cm, what is its diameter?
42. 10% of 360
45. Find x, if $x - 5 = 94$
48. If the ratio of men to women at a local supermarket is 10:25 and there are 125 women, how many men are there? *(Do 125 ÷ 25 first)*
49. 6.5 – 0.6 *(Hint, it's like 65 – 6, then put the . in)*
50. ¹⁄₁₀ as a decimal *(Hint, ²⁄₁₀ = 0.2)*
52. What's next in the sequence? 104, 99, 95, 92

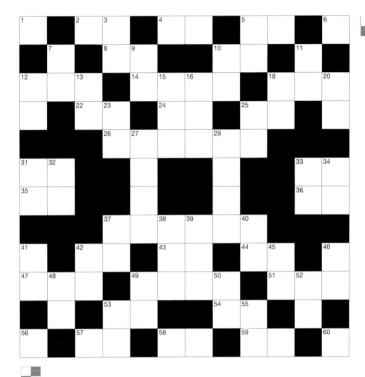

Crossword 4
Levels 5, 6 & 7

make sure you find all 9 decimal points

Clues across

1. 5.8 to 1 significant figure
2. The 5th prime number
4. 7% of £300 *(Hint, find 1% first)*
5. If the ratio of boys to girls in the class is 3:4 how many boys will there be if there are 24 girls in the class? *(Hint, find how many 4s make 24 first)*
6. Simplify $5n + 8 - 2n - 2 - 3n$
8. $2f(19f + 6g) = ?f^2 + 12fg$
10. 2 to the power 4 *(Hint, 2 to the power 5 = 2 x 2 x 2 x 2 x 2)*
12. A pair of gloves cost £8.96 originally. What do they cost in the '25% off sale'?
14. 1269 to the nearest hundred
18. 2.98 + 2.04 *(Hint, do 298 + 204 first)*
22. The mean of 14, 16, 11 and 11
24. 0.6 x 4 *(Hint, it's like 6 x 4)*
25. ⅘ of 90 *(Hint, find ⅕ first)*
26. 3136.12×10^2
31. 35 out of 50 as a %
33. 1% of 6700
35. -5×-5
36. 45 – (–7) *(Hint, what does – – change to?)*
37. 4567.678 to 2 decimal places
42. The perimeter of a square whose side length is 8cm *(Perimeter = length around outside)*
43. If $4q \times 3q = 12q^2$, then $2q \times 5q = ?q^2$
44. Find x, if $2x - 10 = 28$ *(Hint, do the opposite to – 10 to the other side first)*
47. 4.56×10^2
49. 6000 – 110
51. $10^3 - 9$
53. The area in cm² of a square whose length is 7cm
54. Volume of a cuboid 1cm by 2cm by 9cm
56. The nth term of this sequence 7, 9, 11, 13, 15 is 2n + ? *(Hint, it's like the 2x table, but always ? more)*
57. Area of a triangle base 12cm and vertical height 1.3cm *(Hint, halve the base first)*
58. 10% of 670
59. (Surface area of cuboid 10 by 1 by 1) – 9
60. ?/10 is in between the fractions 3/5 and 4/5. Is it a) 6, b) 7, or c) 8?

Clues down

3. 12.96 correct to 2 significant figures
5. Complete the sequence 256, 128, 64, 32
7. How old do you have to be to drive a car in England?
9. 9 squared
10. Cedric the centipede put on 45 pairs of bed socks to keep himself warm. How many of his feet were left uncovered?
11. What is the median of 12, 25, 24, 17, 20
12. 248 divided by 4 *(Hint, do 4s in to 24 first)*
13. A 3 and a 7 sided spinner are spun. The chance of getting a one on both is 1/? *(Hint, it would be ⅑ if both spinners had 3 sides)*
15. (10 x 31) + 13
16. If the chance of Zainah being late for registration at least once this week is 0.54, what's the chance that she won't be?
18. (7 x 8) – (6 x 4) + (2 x 10)
20. 26/50 – 6/50 = ?/50
23. 198 divided by 6
25. Find 75% of 96 *(Hint, find ½ then a ¼ first)*
27. 1.345×10^3 *(Hint, $1.678 \times 10^3 = 1678$)*
29. 11.56×10^2
31. 3m – (2m and 28cm) (give the answer in cm)
32. ⁵⁰⁄₁₀₀ as a decimal *(Hint, ⁴⁰⁄₁₀₀ = 0.4)*
33. If 0.123m = 123mm, what is 0.065m in mm?
34. (7 x 11) – 5
37. 12 + (⅓ of 90)
38. 316 + 302
39. $(7 \times 10 \times 10) + 3^2$
40. What is the next number in the sequence? 1, 3, 9, 27
41. 37 x 2
42. (–3 x –6) + (–2 x –9)
45. Find x, if $2x - 12 = 186$ *(Hint, do the opposite to – 12 to the other side first. It's also a gorgeous ice cream!)*
46. The smallest number whose factors are 1, 3 and 7
48. If the ratio of men to women at a local supermarket is 2:5 and there are 125 women, how many men are there? *(Hint, do 125 ÷ 5 first)*
49. 6.5 – 0.6 *(Hint, it's like 65 – 6)*
50. ¹⁄₁₀ as a decimal *(Hint, ²⁄₁₀ = 0.2)*
52. 104, 99, 95, 92 *(Hint, it's not 89!)*
53. If 5x times $5x = 25x^2$, then 4x times $12x = ?x^2$
55. 90 – (Snow White's ? dwarfs)

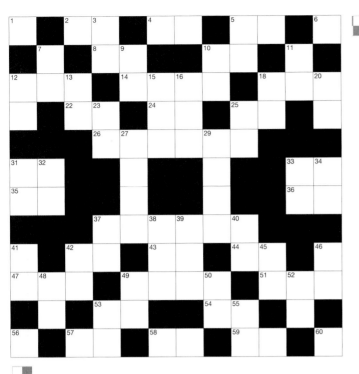

Crossword 4
Levels 6 & 7

make sure you find all 9 decimal points

Clues down

3. 12.96 correct to 2 significant figures
5. Complete the sequence 256, 128, 64, 32
7. How old do you have to be to drive a car in England?
9. $\sqrt{81} \times \sqrt{81}$
10. Cedric the centipede put on 45 pairs of bed socks to keep himself warm at night. How many of his feet were left uncovered?
11. What is the median of 23, 21, 16, 12, 25, 24, 17, 17, 20?
12. Simplify $3x^2 - 4x - x^2 + 62 + 4x - 2x^2$
13. What is $^{21}/_{100}$ as a %?
15. $(11 \times 31) - 18$
16. If the chance of Gary being dumped by Jenny this week is 0.54, what is the chance of him not being dumped?
18. $6^2 + \sqrt{256}$
20. 4 out of 20 as a %
23. $(x + 11)(x - 3) = x^2 + 11x - 3x - ?$
25. 0.25×288
27. 1.345 km = ?m
29. $115600 \div 10^2$
31. 3000mm − 2280mm (give the answer in cm)
32. $^{50}/_{100}$ as a decimal
33. $1.3 \times 0.5 \times 100$
34. When a 9 sided and an 8 sided spinner are spun, the probability of getting two ones is 1/?
37. $(^2/_9$ of 45$) + (^1/_2$ of 64$)$
38. $316 + 302$
39. $(0.7 \times 10 \times 10 \times 10) + 3^2$
40. What is the next number in the sequence? 1, 3, 9, 27
41. 37×2
42. If the nth term of a sequence is $n^2 + 11$, what is the 5th term?
45. Find x, if $2x + 3 = 300 - x$ *(Hint, it's a type of ice cream!)*
46. The smallest number whose factors are 1, 3 and 7
48. If the ratio of men to women at a local super-market is 2:5 and there are 125 women, how many men are there?
49. $6.5 - 0.6$
50. $^1/_{10}$ as a decimal
52. Next in the sequence 104, 99, 95, 92
53. 240 divided by the number of sides in a pentagon
55. $(4 \times 11) + (3 \times 13)$

Clues across

1. 5.8 to 1 significant figure
2. The 5th prime number
4. If x = 2, find $4x^2 + 2x + 1$
5. If the ratio of boys to girls in the class is 3:4 how many boys will there be if there are 24 girls in the class?
6. The nth term in this sequence 9, 12, 15, 18, 21 is 3n + ?
8. 66.6666% of 57
10. $?f^2(3f + 2g) = 48f^3 + 32f^2g$
12. 2.1×3.2
14. 1269 to 2 significant figures
18. If the radius of a circle is 2.51cm, what is the diameter?
22. The mean of 14, 16, 11 and 11
24. 0.06×40
25. 80% of 90
26. 3.13612×10^5
31. 14 out of 20 as a %
33. 1% of 6700
35. $(-5 \times -9) + (-4 \times 5)$
36. If x = −7, find 45 − x
37. 4567.678 to 2 decimal places
42. (The perimeter of a square whose side length is 1.3cm) + 26.8cm
43. The number of planets in our solar system + 1
44. Find x, if $2(x - 6) = x + 7$ *(Hint, expand before getting the xs to one side and the numbers to the other)*
47. $4\,560\,000 \times 10^{-4}$
49. $(20 \times 30 \times 10) - 110$
51. $10^3 - 3^2$
53. The area in cm^2 of a square whose perimeter is 28cm
54. Volume of a cuboid 1½cm by 3cm by 4cm
56. If $12q^2 \div 4q = 3q$, then $25q^2 \div 5q = ?q$
57. Area of a triangle base 12cm and vertical height 1.3cm
58. (Surface area of a cuboid 15 by 1 by 1) + 5
59. 30% of 110
60. ?/10 is in between 3/5 and 4/5

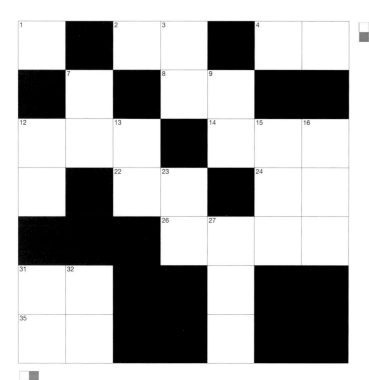

Crossword 5
Level 1

make sure you find all 4 decimal points

Clues across

1. How many years are there between each World Cup football competition?
2. (3 x 4) + 1
4. 10 + 10 + 10 + 5
8. 13♥ – 2♥ = ?♥
12. Which amount of money is biggest? a) £6.39, b) £6.93, or c) £3.96
14. ? + 1 = 124
22. 20 – (2 x 3)
24. Calum the cockroach and his identical twin brother measure 2.6cm each. What do they both measure when put in line? Is it a) 4.4cm, b) 5.2cm, or c) 6.2cm?
26. Write in figures one thousand, three hundred and fifty-seven
31. 15 + 5 + 5 + 5 + 5
35. Is 14 + 14 + 14 + 14 a) 56 or b) 46?

Clues down

3. Is 30.9 closer to 30 or 31?
7. What's the next number in the sequence? 27, 25, 23, 21
9. 22 shared between 2
12. (Half of 20) + 53
13. (½ of 10) + 26
15. 200 + (2 x 5) + 45
16. What's next in this sequence? £3.15, £3.18, £3.21, £3.24
23. (6 shared between 2) + 38
27. 1 + ? = 323
31. 20 + 5 + 5 + 5
32. Which of these numbers is bigger than 5 but less than 6? Is it a) 4.6, b) 5.6, or c) 6.6?

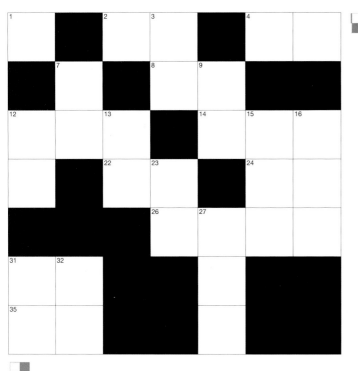

Crossword 5
Levels 1 & 2

make sure you find all 4 decimal points

Clues across

1. How many years are there between each World Cup football competition?
2. (6 x 2) + 11 – (2 x 5)
4. 10 + 10 + 10 + 4 + ½ + ½
8. 13♥ – 2♥ = ?♥
12. £5.00 + £1.93
14. ? + 1 = 124
22. (13 + 15) ÷ 2
24. Calum the cockroach and his identical twin brother measure 2.6cm each. What do they both measure when put in line? Is it a) 4.4cm, b) 5.2cm or c) 6.2cm?
26. 1351 ÷ 6
31. (3 x 3) + (4 x 2) + 20 – 2
35. 4 + ? = 60

Clues down

3. Is 30.9 closer to 30 or 31?
7. What's the next number in the sequence? 27, 25, 23, 21
9. 22 shared between 2
12. (Half of 20) + 53
13. (½ of 10) + 26
15. 200 + (4 x 5) + 35
16. What's next in this sequence? £3.15, £3.18, £3.21, £3.24
23. (9 shared between 3) + 38
27. 324 – ? = 2
31. 5 + 5 + 5 + 5 + 5 + 5 + 5
32. If 57mm = 5.7cm, then what is 56mm in cm?

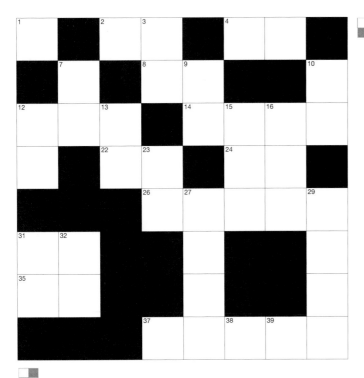

make sure you find all 6 decimal points

Clues across

1. How many years are there between each World Cup football competition?
2. (6 x 2) + 11 − (2 x 5)
4. 10 + 10 + 10 + 4 + ¼ + ¼ + ¼ + ¼
8. 13♠ − 2♠ = ?♠
12. £5.00 + £1.93
14. ? + 1 = 1235
22. (13 + 15) ÷ 2
24. Calum the cockroach and his identical twin brother measure 2.6cm each. What do they both measure when put in line. Is it a) 4.4cm, b) 5.2cm, or c) 5.4cm?
26. What's smallest? a) 1357.8, b) 1537.8, or c) 1753.8
31. The chance that Barry will sulk over the next weekend is 65%. What's the chance he won't? a) 30%, b) 35%, or c) 45%
35. 4 + ? = 60
37. What's smallest? a) 1234.5, b) 1235.4, or c) 1254.3

Clues down

3. Is 30.9 closer to 30 or 31?
7. What's the next number in the sequence? 27, 25, 23, 21
9. 22 shared between 2
10. (50% of 20) + 14
12. (25% of 20) + 58 (Hint, 25% is a ¼)
13. (½ of 10) + 26
15. 200 + (4 x 5) + 35
16. What's next in this sequence? £3.03, £3.09, £3.15, £3.21
23. (15 ÷ 3) + 36
27. 3000 + 222
29. (1000 x 8) + 5
31. If 1% of £500 is £5, what is 7% of £500?
32. If 59mm = 5.9cm, then what is 56mm in cm?

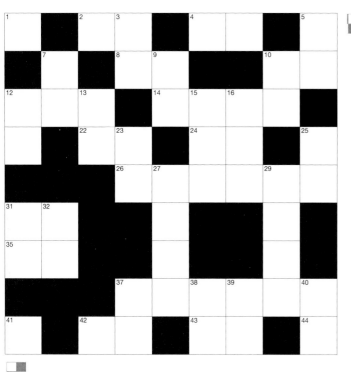

Crossword 5
Levels 2, 3 & 4

make sure you find all 7 decimal points

Clues across

1. How many years are there between each World Cup?
2. Double 6.5
4. 7% of £500 (Hint, find 1% first, by taking off two zeros)
8. (5 x 7) – (6 x 4)
10. If half of something is 12.5, what is its total?
12. £2.31 + £2.31 + £2.31
14. 1235 – 2 = ? – 1
22. Cedric the centipede put on 43 pairs of slippers after his hard day's work at the office. How many feet were left uncovered? (Remember, centi means 100)
24. If 67mm = 6.7cm, what is 52mm in cm?
26. £1350.00 + £7.85
31. 37 – 4 = ? – 2
35. (18 ÷ 3) + 50
37. £1235.00 – 43p
42. The area of a rectangle whose length is 30cm and whose width is 2cm (Hint, area is length x width)
43. Find x if, x + 6 = 20

Clues down

3. $30\mathscr{6} + 3\mathscr{6} - 2\mathscr{6} = ?\mathscr{6}$
5. Complete the sequence 45, 40, 35, 30
7. What century was Queen Victoria crowned in?
9. (The square root of 4) + 9 (Hint, what number x itself makes 4?)
10. If I get 22 out of 100 in a test, that would be 22%. What would 24 out of 100 be?
12. 7 x 9 (Hint, do 7 x 10 then take away 7)
13. (3 x 7) + (2 x 5)
15. (10 x 25) + 5
16. An Easter egg costs £6.54 originally. When it's ½ price, is it a) £3.24, b) £3.27, or c) £3.29?
23. Number of legs on a centipede – 59
25. (⅓ of 6) + 23
27. 32,220 ÷ 10 (Hint, 220 ÷ 10 = 22)
29. The number of legs on 8 millipedes + 5 (Remember, milli means 1000)
31. 7 x 5
32. Complete the sequence 4.8, 5.0, 5.2, 5.4
37. The perimeter of a rectangle 2cm by 3cm (Hint, draw it and add the edges together)
38. Is a quarter of 12.4cm a) 2.5cm, b) 3.1cm, or c) 3.5cm?
39. ½ + ¼ + 40 + 2 + 1¼
40. 8 x 9, or (8 x 10) – 8
41. The chance of Vinnie Jones being a 'hard man' in his next movie is 99%. What's the chance he isn't?

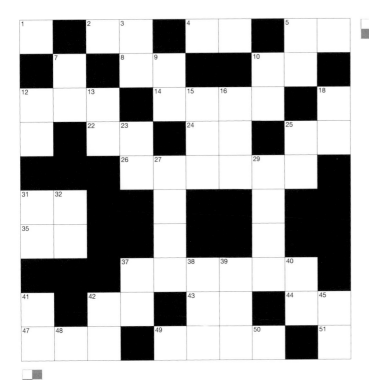

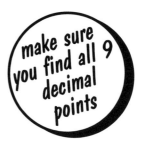

Crossword 5
Levels 3, 4 & 5

make sure you find all 9 decimal points

Clues across

1. Look at the coordinates (1,4), (2,8), (3,12), (4,16). What do you times the first number in each coordinate by to get the second number in each coordinate?
2. What's the next prime number after 11? *(Hint, a prime number has only 2 factors, 1 and itself)*
4. 7% of £500 *(Hint, find 1% first, by taking off two zeros)*
5. The ratio of boys to girls at a party is 1:2. If there are 10 boys, how many girls are there?
8. $(6 \times 6) + (4 \times 9) - 61$
10. If 50% of something is 12.5, what is its total?
12. £2.31 + £2.31 + £2.31
14. $1235 - 2 = ? - 1$
22. Cedric the centipede put on 43 pairs of slippers after his hard day's work at the office. How many feet were left uncovered?
24. $6.3 - 2.4 + 1.3$ *(Hint, do 63 – 24 + 13)*
25. A quarter as a %
26. £1400.00 – £40.00 – £2.15
31. If x = 5, what is 7x?
35. $(36 \div 3) + 44$
37. Is 1234.571 closer to 1234.57 or 1234.58?
42. The area of a rectangle whose length is 30cm and whose width is 2cm *(Hint, area is length x width)*
43. $(? \times 2) + 1 = 29$
44. $2^2 + 4^2$ *(Hint, $3^2 = 9$)*
47. If 55.7 x 10 is 557, what is 56.7 x 10?
49. $(100 - 81) + 5900$

Clues down

3. $30\text{℞} + 12\text{℞} - 11\text{℞} = ?\text{℞}$
5. Complete the sequence 53, 46, 39, 32
7. In what century was Queen Victoria crowned?
9. $\sqrt{4} + 9$ *(Hint, $\sqrt{9} = 3$)*
10. 24 out of 100 as a % *(Hint, 22 out of 100 = 22%)*
12. 7 x 9 *(Hint, do 7 x 10 then take away 7)*
13. $(6 \times 7) + (3 \times 12) - 47$
15. $(10 \times 25) + 5$
16. If two Easter eggs cost £3.24 and £3.30, is their 'mean average' price a) £3.26, b) £3.27, or c) £3.28?
18. Find x, if 2x = 70
23. 123 divided by 3 *(Hint, do 3 into 12 first, then 3s into 3)*
25. $(\frac{1}{3} \text{ of } 6) + 23$
27. 32 220 ÷ 10
29. The number of legs on 8 millipedes + 5
31. 7 x 5
32. What is the next number in the sequence? 8.0, 7.4, 6.8, 6.2 *(Hint, how many does it decrease by each time?)*
37. What's the perimeter or distance around the edges of a rectangle 3cm by 2cm
38. 50% of £6.38
39. $(21 \times 10) + (21 \times 10) + 21$
40. 8 x 9, or (8 x 10) – 8
41. If 140cm = 1.4m, then what is 150cm in m?
42. The chance of Barry sulking during his summer holidays is 33%. What's the chance he doesn't?
45. A scientist cuts a 0.9mm bed bug into 3 equal bits. What does each bit measure?

How to Dazzle at Maths Crosswords Book 1

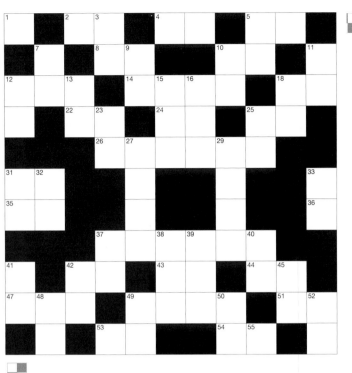

make sure you find all 8 decimal points

Clues across

1. 5.8 to the nearest whole number
2. The 5th prime number *(Hint, the first is 2)*
4. 7% of £300 *(Hint, find 1% first)*
5. If the ratio of boys to girls in the class is 9:12 how many boys will there be if there are 24 girls in the class? *(Hint, see how many 12s are in 24 first, then 2 lots of 12 make 24)*
8. 6 squared + 2
10. $2(8f - 5) = ?f - 10$
12. A pair of gloves cost £8.96 originally. How much are they with 25% off?
14. 1269 to the nearest hundred
18. Is 2.98 + 2.04 closer to a) 5.0 or b) 5.1? *(Hint, do 298 + 204 first)*
22. The mean of 14, 16, 11 and 11 *(Add them all and ÷ by 4)*
24. If 3700g = 3.7kg, what is 2400g in kg?
25. 50% of 144
26. Write three hundred and thirteen thousand, six hundred and twelve in figures
31. 70 out of 100 as a %
35. Area of a square with side length 5cm
37. 4567.679 to 2 decimal places
42. The perimeter of a square whose side length is 8cm *(Perimeter = length around outside)*
43. If $3q \times 2 = 6q$, then $2q \times 5 = ?q$
44. Find x, if $x - 21 = -2$
47. If $8.73 \times 100 = 873$, then what is 4.56×100?
49. 6000 - 110
51. Gorgeous ice cream with cone and flake
53. The area in cm^2 of a square whose length is 7cm
54. Angles in a triangle ÷ 10

Clues down

3. 12.9 to the nearest whole number
5. Simplify $7x - 4 - 3x + 20 - 4x$
7. What's the legal age to drive in England?
9. 9 squared
10. Cedric the centipede put on 45 pairs of bed socks to keep himself warm. How many of his feet were left uncovered?
11. What is the median of 23, 21, 16, 12, 25, 24, 17, 17, 20? *(Hint, put them in order first, then find the middle one)*
12. 248 divided by 4 *(Hint, do 4s into 24 first)*
13. What is $^{21}/_{100}$ as a %? *(Hint, $^{23}/_{100} = 23\%$)*
15. $(10 \times 31) + 13$
16. If the chance of Zainah being late for registration at least once this week is 0.54, what's the chance that she won't be?
18. $64/100 - 12/100 = ?/100$
23. 198 divided by 6 *(Hint, do 6s into 19 first, then carry the 1)*
25. 25% of 288
27. 1.345×1000 *(Hint, $2.345 \times 1000 = 2345$)*
29. 11.56×100
31. 1m - 28cm (give the answer in cm)
32. $^{50}/_{100}$ as a decimal *(Hint, $^{40}/_{100} = 0.4$)*
33. (75% of £40) + £35
37. $12 + (⅓ \text{ of } 90)$
38. 316 + 302
39. $(7 \times 100) + 3^2$
40. What is the next number in the sequence? 1, 3, 9, 27
41. If a circle has a radius of 37cm, what is its diameter?
42. 10% of 360
45. Find x, if $x - 5 = 94$
48. If the ratio of men to women at a local supermarket is 10:25 and there are 125 women, how many men are there? *(Do 125 ÷ 25 first)*
49. 6.5 - 0.6 *(Hint, it's like 65 - 6, then put the . in)*
50. $^1/_{10}$ as a decimal *(Hint, $^2/_{10} = 0.2$)*
52. What's next in the sequence? 104, 99, 95, 92

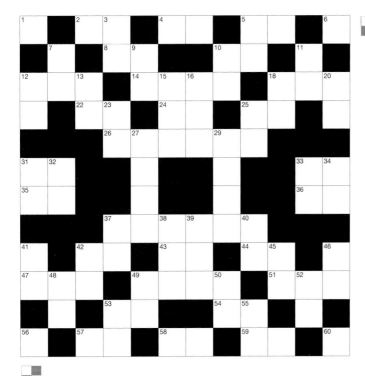

Crossword 4
Levels 5, 6 & 7

make sure you find all 9 decimal points

Clues across

1. 5.8 to 1 significant figure
2. The 5th prime number
4. 7% of £300 *(Hint, find 1% first)*
5. If the ratio of boys to girls in the class is 3:4 how many boys will there be if there are 24 girls in the class? *(Hint, find how many 4s make 24 first)*
6. Simplify $5n + 8 - 2n - 2 - 3n$
8. $2f(19f + 6g) = ?f^2 + 12fg$
10. 2 to the power 4 *(Hint, 2 to the power 5 = 2 x 2 x 2 x 2 x 2)*
12. A pair of gloves cost £8.96 originally. What do they cost in the '25% off sale'?
14. 1269 to the nearest hundred
18. 2.98 + 2.04 *(Hint, do 298 + 204 first)*
22. The mean of 14, 16, 11 and 11
24. 0.6 x 4 *(Hint, it's like 6 x 4)*
25. ⅘ of 90 *(Hint, find ⅕ first)*
26. 3136.12×10^2
31. 35 out of 50 as a %
33. 1% of 6700
35. -5×-5
36. 45 − (−7) *(Hint, what does − − change to?)*
37. 4567.678 to 2 decimal places
42. The perimeter of a square whose side length is 8cm *(Perimeter = length around outside)*
43. If $4q \times 3q = 12q^2$, then $2q \times 5q = ?q^2$
44. Find x, if $2x - 10 = 28$ *(Hint, do the opposite to − 10 to the other side first)*
47. 4.56×10^2
49. 6000 − 110
51. $10^3 - 9$
53. The area in cm² of a square whose length is 7cm
54. Volume of a cuboid 1cm by 2cm by 9cm
56. The nth term of this sequence 7, 9, 11, 13, 15 is 2n + ? *(Hint, it's like the 2x table, but always ? more)*
57. Area of a triangle base 12cm and vertical height 1.3cm *(Hint, halve the base first)*
58. 10% of 670
59. (Surface area of cuboid 10 by 1 by 1) − 9
60. ?/10 is in between the fractions 3/5 and 4/5. Is it a) 6, b) 7, or c) 8?

Clues down

3. 12.96 correct to 2 significant figures
5. Complete the sequence 256, 128, 64, 32
7. How old do you have to be to drive a car in England?
9. 9 squared
10. Cedric the centipede put on 45 pairs of bed socks to keep himself warm. How many of his feet were left uncovered?
11. What is the median of 12, 25, 24, 17, 20
12. 248 divided by 4 *(Hint, do 4s in to 24 first)*
13. A 3 and a 7 sided spinner are spun. The chance of getting a one on both is 1/? *(Hint, it would be ⅑ if both spinners had 3 sides)*
15. (10 x 31) + 13
16. If the chance of Zainah being late for registration at least once this week is 0.54, what's the chance that she won't be?
18. (7 x 8) − (6 x 4) + (2 x 10)
20. 26/50 − 6/50 = ?/50
23. 198 divided by 6
25. Find 75% of 96 *(Hint, find ½ then a ¼ first)*
27. 1.345×10^3 *(Hint, $1.678 \times 10^3 = 1678$)*
29. 11.56×10^2
31. 3m − (2m and 28cm) (give the answer in cm)
32. 50/100 as a decimal *(Hint, 40/100 = 0.4)*
33. If 0.123m = 123mm, what is 0.065m in mm?
34. (7 x 11) − 5
37. 12 + (⅓ of 90)
38. 316 + 302
39. $(7 \times 10 \times 10) + 3^2$
40. What is the next number in the sequence? 1, 3, 9, 27
41. 37 x 2
42. (−3 x −6) + (−2 x −9)
45. Find x, if $2x - 12 = 186$ *(Hint, do the opposite to − 12 to the other side first. It's also a gorgeous ice cream!)*
46. The smallest number whose factors are 1, 3 and 7
48. If the ratio of men to women at a local super-market is 2:5 and there are 125 women, how many men are there? *(Hint, do 125 ÷ 5 first)*
49. 6.5 − 0.6 *(Hint, it's like 65 − 6)*
50. 1/10 as a decimal *(Hint, 2/10 = 0.2)*
52. 104, 99, 95, 92 *(Hint, it's not 89!)*
53. If 5x times 5x = 25x², then 4x times 12x = ?x²
55. 90 − (Snow White's ? dwarfs)

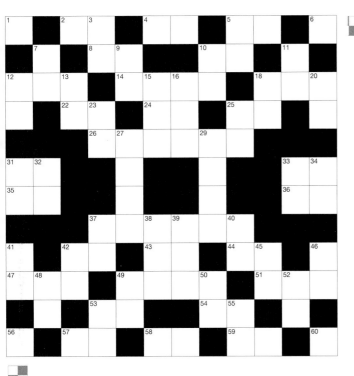

Crossword 4 Levels 6 & 7

make sure you find all 9 decimal points

Clues down

3. 12.96 correct to 2 significant figures
5. Complete the sequence 256, 128, 64, 32
7. How old do you have to be to drive a car in England?
9. $\sqrt{81} \times \sqrt{81}$
10. Cedric the centipede put on 45 pairs of bed socks to keep himself warm at night. How many of his feet were left uncovered?
11. What is the median of 23, 21, 16, 12, 25, 24, 17, 17, 20?
12. Simplify $3x^2 - 4x - x^2 + 62 + 4x - 2x^2$
13. What is $^{21}/_{100}$ as a %?
15. $(11 \times 31) - 18$
16. If the chance of Gary being dumped by Jenny this week is 0.54, what is the chance of him not being dumped?
18. $6^2 + \sqrt{256}$
20. 4 out of 20 as a %
23. $(x + 11)(x - 3) = x^2 + 11x - 3x - ?$
25. 0.25×288
27. 1.345 km = ?m
29. $115600 \div 10^2$
31. 3000mm − 2280mm (give the answer in cm)
32. $^{50}/_{100}$ as a decimal
33. $1.3 \times 0.5 \times 100$
34. When a 9 sided and an 8 sided spinner are spun, the probability of getting two ones is 1/?
37. $(^2/_9 \text{ of } 45) + (½ \text{ of } 64)$
38. $316 + 302$
39. $(0.7 \times 10 \times 10 \times 10) + 3^2$
40. What is the next number in the sequence? 1, 3, 9, 27
41. 37×2
42. If the nth term of a sequence is $n^2 + 11$, what is the 5th term?
45. Find x, if $2x + 3 = 300 - x$ (Hint, it's a type of ice cream!)
46. The smallest number whose factors are 1, 3 and 7
48. If the ratio of men to women at a local supermarket is 2:5 and there are 125 women, how many men are there?
49. $6.5 - 0.6$
50. $^1/_{10}$ as a decimal
52. Next in the sequence 104, 99, 95, 92
53. 240 divided by the number of sides in a pentagon
55. $(4 \times 11) + (3 \times 13)$

Clues across

1. 5.8 to 1 significant figure
2. The 5th prime number
4. If x = 2, find $4x^2 + 2x + 1$
5. If the ratio of boys to girls in the class is 3:4 how many boys will there be if there are 24 girls in the class?
6. The nth term in this sequence 9, 12, 15, 18, 21 is 3n + ?
8. 66.6666% of 57
10. $?f^2(3f + 2g) = 48f^3 + 32f^2g$
12. 2.1×3.2
14. 1269 to 2 significant figures
18. If the radius of a circle is 2.51cm, what is the diameter?
22. The mean of 14, 16, 11 and 11
24. 0.06×40
25. 80% of 90
26. 3.13612×10^5
31. 14 out of 20 as a %
33. 1% of 6700
35. $(-5 \times -9) + (-4 \times 5)$
36. If x = −7, find 45 − x
37. 4567.678 to 2 decimal places
42. (The perimeter of a square whose side length is 1.3cm) + 26.8cm
43. The number of planets in our solar system + 1
44. Find x, if $2(x - 6) = x + 7$ (Hint, expand before getting the xs to one side and the numbers to the other)
47. $4\,560\,000 \times 10^{-4}$
49. $(20 \times 30 \times 10) - 110$
51. $10^3 - 3^2$
53. The area in cm^2 of a square whose perimeter is 28cm
54. Volume of a cuboid 1½cm by 3cm by 4cm
56. If $12q^2 \div 4q = 3q$, then $25q^2 \div 5q = ?q$
57. Area of a triangle base 12cm and vertical height 1.3cm
58. (Surface area of a cuboid 15 by 1 by 1) + 5
59. 30% of 110
60. ?/10 is in between 3/5 and 4/5

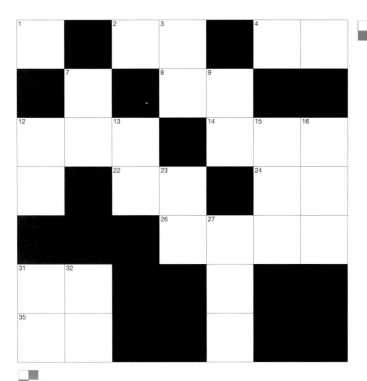

make sure you find all 4 decimal points

Clues across

1. How many years are there between each World Cup football competition?
2. $(3 \times 4) + 1$
4. $10 + 10 + 10 + 5$
8. $13\heartsuit - 2\heartsuit = ?\heartsuit$
12. Which amount of money is biggest? a) £6.39, b) £6.93, or c) £3.96
14. $? + 1 = 124$
22. $20 - (2 \times 3)$
24. Calum the cockroach and his identical twin brother measure 2.6cm each. What do they both measure when put in line? Is it a) 4.4cm, b) 5.2cm, or c) 6.2cm?
26. Write in figures one thousand, three hundred and fifty-seven
31. $15 + 5 + 5 + 5 + 5$
35. Is $14 + 14 + 14 + 14$ a) 56 or b) 46?

Clues down

3. Is 30.9 closer to 30 or 31?
7. What's the next number in the sequence? 27, 25, 23, 21
9. 22 shared between 2
12. (Half of 20) + 53
13. (½ of 10) + 26
15. $200 + (2 \times 5) + 45$
16. What's next in this sequence? £3.15, £3.18, £3.21, £3.24
23. (6 shared between 2) + 38
27. $1 + ? = 323$
31. $20 + 5 + 5 + 5$
32. Which of these numbers is bigger than 5 but less than 6? Is it a) 4.6, b) 5.6, or c) 6.6?

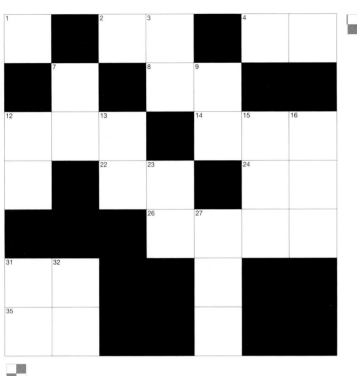

Crossword 5
Levels 1 & 2

make sure you find all 4 decimal points

Clues across

1. How many years are there between each World Cup football competition?
2. (6 x 2) + 11 – (2 x 5)
4. 10 + 10 + 10 + 4 + ½ + ½
8. 13♥ – 2♥ = ?♥
12. £5.00 + £1.93
14. ? + 1 = 124
22. (13 + 15) ÷ 2
24. Calum the cockroach and his identical twin brother measure 2.6cm each. What do they both measure when put in line? Is it a) 4.4cm, b) 5.2cm or c) 6.2cm?
26. 1351 + 6
31. (3 x 3) + (4 x 2) + 20 – 2
35. 4 + ? = 60

Clues down

3. Is 30.9 closer to 30 or 31?
7. What's the next number in the sequence? 27, 25, 23, 21
9. 22 shared between 2
12. (Half of 20) + 53
13. (½ of 10) + 26
15. 200 + (4 x 5) + 35
16. What's next in this sequence? £3.15, £3.18, £3.21, £3.24
23. (9 shared between 3) + 38
27. 324 – ? = 2
31. 5 + 5 + 5 + 5 + 5 + 5 + 5
32. If 57mm = 5.7cm, then what is 56mm in cm?

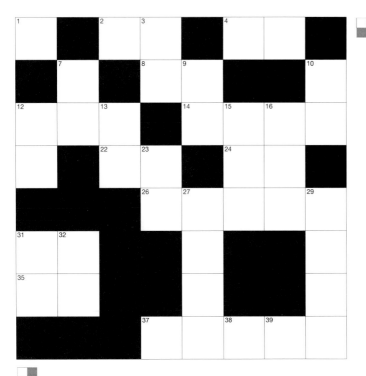

Crossword 5
Levels 2 & 3

make sure you find all 6 decimal points

Clues across

1. How many years are there between each World Cup football competition?
2. (6 x 2) + 11 – (2 x 5)
4. 10 + 10 + 10 + 4 + ¼ + ¼ + ¼ + ¼
8. 13🐜 – 2🐜 = ?🐜
12. £5.00 + £1.93
14. ? + 1 = 1235
22. (13 + 15) ÷ 2
24. Calum the cockroach and his identical twin brother measure 2.6cm each. What do they both measure when put in line. Is it a) 4.4cm, b) 5.2cm, or c) 5.4cm?
26. What's smallest? a) 1357.8, b) 1537.8, or c) 1753.8
31. The chance that Barry will sulk over the next weekend is 65%. What's the chance he won't? a) 30%, b) 35%, or c) 45%
35. 4 + ? = 60
37. What's smallest? a) 1234.5, b) 1235.4, or c) 1254.3

Clues down

3. Is 30.9 closer to 30 or 31?
7. What's the next number in the sequence? 27, 25, 23, 21
9. 22 shared between 2
10. (50% of 20) + 14
12. (25% of 20) + 58 (Hint, 25% is a ¼)
13. (½ of 10) + 26
15. 200 + (4 x 5) + 35
16. What's next in this sequence? £3.03, £3.09, £3.15, £3.21
23. (15 ÷ 3) + 36
27. 3000 + 222
29. (1000 x 8) + 5
31. If 1% of £500 is £5, what is 7% of £500?
32. If 59mm = 5.9cm, then what is 56mm in cm?

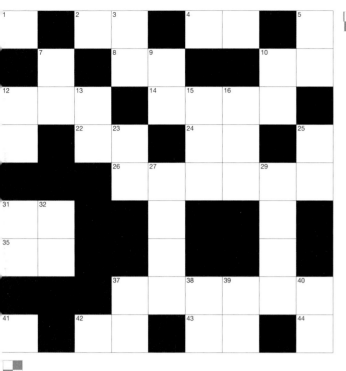

Crossword 5
Levels 2, 3 & 4

make sure you find all 7 decimal points

Clues across

1. How many years are there between each World Cup?
2. Double 6.5
4. 7% of £500 *(Hint, find 1% first, by taking off two zeros)*
8. (5 x 7) – (6 x 4)
10. If half of something is 12.5, what is its total?
12. £2.31 + £2.31 + £2.31
14. 1235 – 2 = ? – 1
22. Cedric the centipede put on 43 pairs of slippers after his hard day's work at the office. How many feet were left uncovered? *(Remember, centi means 100)*
24. If 67mm = 6.7cm, what is 52mm in cm?
26. £1350.00 + £7.85
31. 37 – 4 = ? – 2
35. (18 ÷ 3) + 50
37. £1235.00 – 43p
42. The area of a rectangle whose length is 30cm and whose width is 2cm *(Hint, area is length x width)*
43. Find x if, x + 6 = 20

Clues down

3. 30 + 3 – 2 = ?
5. Complete the sequence 45, 40, 35, 30
7. What century was Queen Victoria crowned in?
9. (The square root of 4) + 9 *(Hint, what number x itself makes 4?)*
10. If I get 22 out of 100 in a test, that would be 22%. What would 24 out of 100 be?
12. 7 x 9 *(Hint, do 7 x 10 then take away 7)*
13. (3 x 7) + (2 x 5)
15. (10 x 25) + 5
16. An Easter egg costs £6.54 originally. When it's ½ price, is it a) £3.24, b) £3.27, or c) £3.29?
23. Number of legs on a centipede – 59
25. (⅓ of 6) + 23
27. 32,220 ÷ 10 *(Hint, 220 ÷ 10 = 22)*
29. The number of legs on 8 millipedes + 5 *(Remember, milli means 1000)*
31. 7 x 5
32. Complete the sequence 4.8, 5.0, 5.2, 5.4
37. The perimeter of a rectangle 2cm by 3cm *(Hint, draw it and add the edges together)*
38. Is a quarter of 12.4cm a) 2.5cm, b) 3.1cm, or c) 3.5cm?
39. ½ + ¼ + 40 + 2 + 1¼
40. 8 x 9, or (8 x 10) – 8
41. The chance of Vinnie Jones being a 'hard man' in his next movie is 99%. What's the chance he isn't?

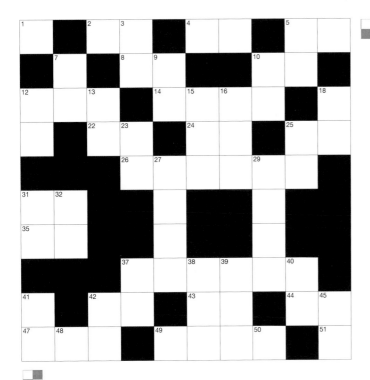

Crossword 5
Levels 3, 4 & 5

make sure you find all 9 decimal points

Clues across

1. Look at the coordinates (1,4), (2,8), (3,12), (4,16). What do you times the first number in each coordinate by to get the second number in each coordinate?
2. What's the next prime number after 11? *(Hint, a prime number has only 2 factors, 1 and itself)*
4. 7% of £500 *(Hint, find 1% first, by taking off two zeros)*
5. The ratio of boys to girls at a party is 1:2. If there are 10 boys, how many girls are there?
8. $(6 \times 6) + (4 \times 9) - 61$
10. If 50% of something is 12.5, what is its total?
12. £2.31 + £2.31 + £2.31
14. $1235 - 2 = ? - 1$
22. Cedric the centipede put on 43 pairs of slippers after his hard day's work at the office. How many feet were left uncovered?
24. $6.3 - 2.4 + 1.3$ *(Hint, do 63 – 24 + 13)*
25. A quarter as a %
26. £1400.00 – £40.00 – £2.15
31. If x = 5, what is 7x?
35. $(36 \div 3) + 44$
37. Is 1234.571 closer to 1234.57 or 1234.58?
42. The area of a rectangle whose length is 30cm and whose width is 2cm *(Hint, area is length x width)*
43. $(? \times 2) + 1 = 29$
44. $2^2 + 4^2$ *(Hint, $3^2 = 9$)*
47. If 55.7×10 is 557, what is 56.7×10?
49. $(100 - 81) + 5900$

Clues down

3. $30 \cancel{P} + 12 \cancel{P} - 11 \cancel{P} = ? \cancel{P}$
5. Complete the sequence 53, 46, 39, 32
7. In what century was Queen Victoria crowned?
9. $\sqrt{4} + 9$ *(Hint, $\sqrt{9} = 3$)*
10. 24 out of 100 as a % *(Hint, 22 out of 100 = 22%)*
12. 7×9 *(Hint, do 7 x 10 then take away 7)*
13. $(6 \times 7) + (3 \times 12) - 47$
15. $(10 \times 25) + 5$
16. If two Easter eggs cost £3.24 and £3.30, is their 'mean average' price a) £3.26, b) £3.27, or c) £3.28?
18. Find x, if 2x = 70
23. 123 divided by 3 *(Hint, do 3 into 12 first, then 3s into 3)*
25. $(\frac{1}{3} \text{ of } 6) + 23$
27. $32\,220 \div 10$
29. The number of legs on 8 millipedes + 5
31. 7×5
32. What is the next number in the sequence? 8.0, 7.4, 6.8, 6.2 *(Hint, how many does it decrease by each time?)*
37. What's the perimeter or distance around the edges of a rectangle 3cm by 2cm
38. 50% of £6.38
39. $(21 \times 10) + (21 \times 10) + 21$
40. 8×9, or $(8 \times 10) - 8$
41. If 140cm = 1.4m, then what is 150cm in m?
42. The chance of Barry sulking during his summer holidays is 33%. What's the chance he doesn't?
45. A scientist cuts a 0.9mm bed bug into 3 equal bits. What does each bit measure?

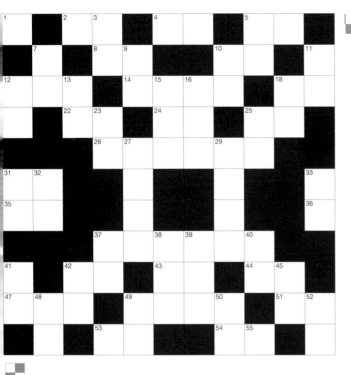

make sure you find all 10 decimal points

Clues across

1. The coordinates (0,0), (1,4), (2,8), (3,12) lie on the line y = ?x *(Hint, what do you times the first number by to get the second?)*
2. What's the next prime number after 11?
4. 7% of £500 *(Hint, find 1% first)*
5. If the ratio of boys to girls at a party is 3:5 and there are 12 boys, how many girls are there? *(Hint, how many lots of 3 make 12?)*
8. √36 + √25
10. If 4 x 6q = 24q, then 5 x 5q = ?q
12. (11 x 33p) + £3.30
14. If x – 1234 = 0, what is x?
18. (How many pairs of trainers are worn by the centipede netball team?) – 315
22. The mean of 15, 17, 12 and 12 *(Add them and divide by 4)*
24. Is the perimeter of a square with length 1.3cm a) 2.6cm, b) 4.6cm, or c) 5.2cm
25. 4/5 = 20/? *(What did I times the 4 by to get 20?)*
26. £1500 – £142.15
31. If 0.23 = 23%, what is 0.35 as a %?
33. 2½% of 200
35. 7 x 8
36. √36 – 1
37. 1234.569 to 2 decimal places
42. The area of a triangle whose base is 20cm and has a vertical height of 6cm *(Hint, half base x height)*
43. Find x, if x + 26 = 40
44. (20 x 10) ÷ 10
47. 56.7 x 10
49. 6000 – 81
51. The sum of the angles in a triangle – 144
53. The area in cm² of a square whose length is 8cm
54. 27 – 1²

Clues down

3. 30.96 correct to 2 significant figures
5. Complete the sequence 45, 40, 35, 30
7. In what century was Queen Victoria crowned?
9. (The square root of 100) + 1
10. 24 out of 100 as a % *(Hint, 22 out of 100 = 22%)*
11. What is the mode of 13, 11, 16, 15, 25, 24, 15, 15, 20? *(Hint, mode means most popular)*
12. If x = 7, find 5x + 28
13. 20½ + 4¼ + 1¾ + ¼ + 4¼
15. (10 x 25) + 5
16. What is the mean of 3.26 and 3.28? *(Hint, it's in the middle of them)*
18. Find x, if 2x = 70
23. 123 divided by 3 *(Hint, do 3 into 12 first)*
25. 5(3f – 5) = 15f – ?
27. 32.22 x 100 *(Hint, move the decimal point)*
29. 800.5 x 10
31. The coordinate (30,?) lies on the line y = x + 5 *(Hint, what is the y part of the coordinate when the x part is 30?)*
32. Complete the sequence 8.4, 7.7, 7.0, 6.3 *(Hint, look at the difference between each number)*
33. 5 x 1.1
37. Volume of a box 2cm by 1cm by 5cm
38. 4 – 0.81 *(Hint, it's like 400 – 81)*
39. 21 x 21 *(Hint, do 21 x 10, then double it, now add 21)*
40. 8 x 9
41. Two angles of a triangle are 90° and 88.5°. What is the third?
42. 10% of 670 *(Hint 10% of 6,700 = 670)*
45. 30 out of 100, as a decimal *(Hint, 40 out of 100 is 0.4)*
48. The ratio of Reebok© to Nike© trainers worn by schoolchildren on a mufti day is 5:6. If 50 people wore Reebok© trainers, how many wore Nike©? *(Hint, what do you times 5 by to get 50?)*
49. What's the 10th term in this series? 9, 14, 19, 24
50. (9 x 10) + 2
52. 3/8 x 7/8 = 21/? *(Hint, I multiplied 3 and 7 to get 21, so what should I do to the 8s?)*

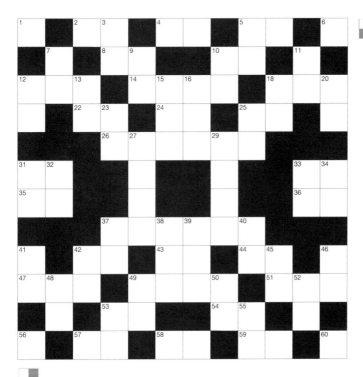

make sure you find all 11 decimal points

59. 40% of 110 *(Hint, find 10% first)*
60. 3/10 − 1/5 = ?/10 *(Hint, how many tenths is 1 fifth?)*

Clues down

3. 30.96 correct to 2 significant figures
5. Complete the sequence −85, −70, −55, −40
7. In what century was Queen Victoria crowned?
9. (The square root of 144) − 1
10. 12 out of 50 as a %
11. What is the mode of 13, 11, 16, 15, 25, 24, 15, 15, 20? *(Hint, mode means most popular)*
12. 25% of 252
13. What is $^{31}/_{100}$ as a %? *(Hint, $^{37}/_{100}$ = 37%)*
15. (10 x 25) + √25
16. What is the mean of 3.26 and 3.28? *(Hint, what's in the middle of them?)*
18. Find x, if x/7 = 5
20. If the probability of Kylie Minogue's next single going to number 1 is 0.3, what's the chance it won't?
23. 246 divided by 6
25. $^5/_7$ of 35 *(Hint, find $^1/_7$ first)*
27. 3.222×10^3 *(Hint, move the decimal point)*
29. 80.05m in cm *(Hint, 7.20m = 720cm)*
31. The coordinate (30,?) lies on the line y = x + 5. What is the y part of the coordinate?
32. What's the next term in the sequence? 7.8, 7.1, 6.5, 6.0
33. 0.5 x 11 *(Hint, do 5 x 11 then put in the point)*
34. The perimeter of a rectangle 24 long and 9 wide
37. (4 x 2 x 30) ÷ (3 x 4 x 2)
38. 4 − 0.81 *(Hint, it's like 400 − 81)*
39. 21^2 *(Hint, do 21 x 10 first)*
40. $2^3 \times 3^2$
41. A right-angled triangle has another angle of 88.5°. What's the third angle?
42. 10% of 670
45. 30 out of 100, as a decimal
46. The number of bowls in 10 overs of cricket
48. The ratio of Reebok© to Nike© trainers worn by schoolchildren on a mufti day is 5:6. If 110 people wore those brands of trainers, how many wore Nike©? *(Hint, how many lots of 5 + 6 = 11 are there?)*
49. The coordinate (30,?) lies on the line x + y = 84. Complete the coordinate?
50. $^{46}/_{50}$ as a %
52. 3/8 x 7/8 = 21/? *(Hint, 2/7 x 6/7 = 12/49)*
53. $10^2 − 6^2$
55. √16 x (√64 + √64)

Clues across

1. The coordinates (0,0), (1,4), (2,8), (3,12) lie on the line y = ?x *(Hint, what do you times the x part by to get the y part?)*
2. The 6th prime number *(The first prime number is 2)*
4. 7% of £500 *(Hint, find 1% first)*
5. If the ratio of boys to girls at a party is 3:5 and there are 32 people in total, how many girls are there? *(Hint, how many groups of the 3+5=8 do you need?)*
6. 9x − 6 − 6x + 10 − 3x
8. The square root of 121
10. If 4q x 6q = $24q^2$, then 5q x 5q = $?q^2$
12. 21 x 33p (in pounds) *(Hint, do 10 x 33p first)*
14. If 4x − 1234 = 3x, what is x?
18. How many pairs of trainers are worn by the centipede netball team?
22. The mean of 15, 17, 12 and 12
24. 1.3 x 4 *(Hint, do 13 x 4, then put the point in)*
25. 4/5 = 20/? *(What did I multiply the 4 by to get 20?)*
26. What's halfway between 1357.8 and 1357.9?
31. 0.35 as a %
33. 1% of 5600
35. If x = −8 and y = −7, what is x times y, or xy? *(Remember, a minus x a minus = a plus)*
36. If x = −11, find 45 − x *(Remember, if you take away a negative, it's like adding)*
37. 1234.569 to 2 decimal places
42. The area of a triangle whose base is 20cm and has a vertical height of 6cm
43. Find x, if 2(x + 6) = 40 *(Hint, divide 40 by 2 first)*
44. (400 x 3) ÷ 60 *(Hint, cancel the noughts first)*
47. 5.67×10^2
49. $6000 − 9^2$
51. The sum of the angles in a parallelogram
53. The area in cm^2 of a square whose length is 8cm
54. $3^3 − 1^2$
56. 16fg + 12f = ?f(4g + 3)
57. 2/3 x 7/8 = 14/? *(Hint, 2/3 x 6/7 = 12/21)*
58. 10% of 780

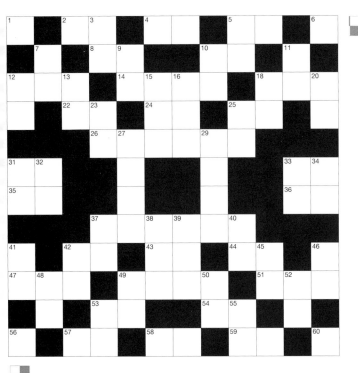

make sure you find all 11 decimal points

Clues down

3. 30.96 correct to 2 significant figures
5. The next term in the sequence –35, –20, –5, 10
7. In what century was Queen Victoria crowned?
9. (The square root of 169) – 2
10. Only 4 out of 60 pupils said their favourite subject was French. What angle would represent them on a pie chart?
11. $x^2 + 16x + 15 = (x + 1)(x + ?)$
12. Area of a trapezium with top = 6.2cm, bottom = 6.4cm and vertical height 10cm
13. What is $^{93}/_{300}$ as a %
15. $(10 \times 25) + \sqrt{25}$
16. What is the mean of 3.26 and 3.28
18. Find x, if $(2x + 2) \div 12 = 6$
20. If the probability of Kylie Minogue's next single going to number 1 is 0.3, what's the chance that it doesn't?
23. The nth term of a sequence is 6n – 1. What is the 7th term?
25. $^5/_7$ of 35
27. 3.222kg in g
29. 80.05m in cm
31. The coordinate (4,?) lies on the line $y = 2x^2 + 3$. What is the y part of the coordinate? *(Hint, it is not 67)*
32. Complete the sequence 7.8, 7.1, 6.5, 6.0
33. 0.5 x 11
34. The perimeter of a rectangle 24 long and 9 wide
37. $(40 \times 20 \times 30) \div (30 \times 40 \times 2)$
38. 4 – (0.9 x 0.9) *(Hint, 0.7 x 0.7 = 0.49)*
39. 21^2
40. $2^3 \times 3^2$
41. 3% of 50p
42. 10% of 670
45. 60 out of 200, as a decimal
46. Minutes in a day ÷ hours in a day
48. The ratio of Reebok© to Nike© trainers worn by schoolchildren on a mufti day is 5:6. If 110 people wore those brands of trainers, how many wore Nike©?
49. The coordinate (30,?) lies on the line $x + y = 84$. Complete the coordinate.
50. (Gorgeous ice cream with a cone and a flake) – 7
52. $3/8 \times 7/8 = 21/?$
53. 384 divided by the number of sides in a hexagon
55. $\sqrt{16} \times 2^2 \times 2^2$

Clues across

1. The coordinates (0,3), (1,7), (2,11), (3,15) lie on the line $y = ?x + 3$
2. The 6th prime number
4. 7% of £500
5. If the ratio of boys to girls at a party is 3:5 and there are 32 people in total, how many girls are there?
6. Expand and simplify $3(3x – 2) – 9x + 10$
8. The square root of 121
10. If $7^{-2} = 1/49$, then $5^{-2} = 1/?$
12. 21p x 33 (give your answer in pounds)
14. If $4x – 1230 = 3x + 4$, what is x?
18. How many pairs of trainers are worn by the centipede netball team?
22. The mean of 15, 17, 12 and 12
24. 0.13 x 40
25. $1/3 + 6/7 = ?/21$ *(Hint, it's an improper fraction)*
26. What's in between 1357.8 and 1357.9?
31. 7 out of 20 as a %
33. 3½% of 1600
35. If x = –9 and y = –8, find $xy + 2y$
36. If x = –11, find 45 – x
37. 1234.567 to 2 decimal places
42. The area of a triangle whose base is 80cm and has a vertical height of 1.5cm
43. Find x, if $4(x – 6) = 2x + 4$ *(Hint, expand before getting xs to one side and numbers to the other)*
44. $(20 \times 20 \times 3) \div 60$
47. 5.67×10^2
49. $(60 \times 10^2) – 9^2$
51. The sum of the angles in a parallelogram
53. The area in cm² of a square whose length is 8cm
54. If a coin and a 13 sided spinner are spun, the chance of getting a 'head and 1' is 1/?
56. $16fg^2 + 12fg$ factorised = $?fg(4g + 3)$
57. $2/3 \times 7/8 = 14/?$
58. $13q \times 6q = ?q^2$ *(Hint, 4q x 6q = 24q²)*
59. 40% of 110
60. $3/10 – 1/5 = ?/10$

Crossword 1 answers

Column headers (top): Levels 1 & 2 | Levels 2 & 3 | Levels 2, 3 & 4 | Levels 3, 4 & 5 | Levels 4, 5 & 6 | Levels 5, 6 & 7

¹7	■	²2	³1	■	⁴1	0	■	⁵6	2	■	⁶2
■	⁷2	■	⁸6	⁹7	■	■	¹⁰1	6	■	¹¹1	■
¹²5	7•9	¹³	■	¹⁴0•1	¹⁵2	¹⁶5	■	¹⁸5	4	²⁰5	
²¹1	■	²²2	²³7	■	²⁴1•2	■	²⁵1	5	■	0	
■	■	²⁶6	²⁷1	4	6	²⁹1	2	■	■		
³¹5	³²4	■	4	■	■	3	■	³³8	³⁴2		
Levels 1 & 2 ³⁵8	6	■	0	■	■	6	■	³⁶1	8		
Levels 2 & 3	■	³⁷5	³⁸0	³⁹0	0	0	⁴⁰0				
Levels 2, 3 & 4 ⁴¹1	■	⁴²2	4	■	⁴³5	0	■	⁴⁴9	⁴⁵2	■	⁴⁶1
Levels 3, 4 & 5 ⁴⁷1	⁴⁸3	2	■	⁴⁹8	8•7	⁵⁰0	■	⁵¹9	⁵²7	5	
Levels 4, 5 & 6	0	■	⁵³4	1	■	■	⁵⁴7	⁵⁵2	■	0	■
Levels 5, 6 & 7 ⁵⁶6	■	⁵⁷0•6	■	⁵⁸2	0	■	⁵⁹1	2	■	⁶⁰1	

Crossword 2 answers

Column headers (top, right side):
- Levels 1 & 2
- Levels 2 & 3
- Levels 2, 3 & 4
- Levels 3, 4 & 5
- Levels 4, 5 & 6
- Levels 5, 6 & 7

Grid answers (by clue number):

Row 1	1=**3**, 2=**1**, 3=**1**, 4=**2 4**, 5=**2 5**, 6=**2**
Row 2	7=**3**, 8=**1**, 9=**9**, 10=**7 8**, 11=**1**
Row 3	12=**7 0 0**, 13=**0**, 14=**4 3 0 0** (14,15,16), 18=**4 9**, 20=**2**
Row 4	12=**0**, 22=**5**, 23=**5**, 24=**3 8**, 25=**1 1**, 20=**5**
Row 5	26=**4 0 7 6**, 29=**0 4**, =**0**
Row 6	31=**9**, 32=**0**, 27=**2**, 29=**0**, 33=**6 4**
Row 7	35=**7 5**, 27=**2**, 29=**0**, 36=**3 2**

Left-side row labels:
- Levels 1 & 2
- Levels 2 & 3 : 37=**3 4 5 6 • 7**, 40=**9**
- Levels 2, 3 & 4 : 41=**2**, 42=**1 8**, 43=**8 0**, 44=**4**, 45=**0**, 46=**5**
- Levels 3, 4 & 5 : 47=**2 5 0**, 49=**2 0 0 0**, 50=**0**, 51=**1**, 52=**0 0**
- Levels 4, 5 & 6 : =**3**, 53=**1 3**, 54=**3**, 55=**0**, =**6**
- Levels 5, 6 & 7 : 56=**3**, 57=**1 3**, 58=**8 0**, 59=**6 0**, 60=**3**

How to Dazzle at Maths Crosswords Book 1

Crossword 3 answers

Column headers (top, right side):
- Levels 1 & 2
- Levels 2 & 3
- Levels 2, 3 & 4
- Levels 3, 4 & 5
- Levels 4, 5 & 6
- Levels 5, 6 & 7

Row labels (left side): Levels 1 & 2 · Levels 2 & 3 · Levels 2, 3 & 4 · Levels 3, 4 & 5 · Levels 4, 5 & 6 · Levels 5, 6 & 7

Grid answers:

1		2	3		4			5			6
5	■	2	1	■	1	2	■	3•0	0	■	5
■	7 2	■	8 5	9 1	■	■	10 3	2	■	11 1	■
12 3•1	13 5	■	■	14 1	15 2	16 4	0	■	18 7•4	5	20 5
0	■	22 2	23 9	■	24 3•2	■	■	25 4	5	■	5
■	■	■	26 4	27 1	4	3	29 1	8	■	■	■
31 8	32 0	■	■	5	■	■	4	■	33 5	34 2
35 8	5	■	■	0	■	■	6	■	36 1	2

Levels 2 & 3: 37 1 0 · 38 0 0 · 39 0 · 40 0

Levels 2, 3 & 4: 41 1 · 42 3 6 · 43 1•5 · 44 7 · 45 5 · 46 1

Levels 3, 4 & 5: 47 5 4 6 · 49 5 8 7 · 50 0 · 51 3 · 52 0•0

Levels 4, 5 & 6: 0 · 53 3 4 · 54 1 2 · 7

Levels 5, 6 & 7: 56 7 · 57 2 1 · 58 4 8 · 59 4 0 · 60 1

Crossword 4 answers

Column headings (left to right): Levels 1 & 2 · Levels 2 & 3 · Levels 2, 3 & 4 · Levels 3, 4 & 5 · Levels 4, 5 & 6 · Levels 5, 6 & 7

								Levels 1 & 2	Levels 2 & 3	Levels 2, 3 & 4	Levels 3, 4 & 5	Levels 4, 5 & 6	Levels 5, 6 & 7
1 6	■	**2** 1	**3** 1	■	**4** 2	1	■	**5** 1	8	■	**6** 6
■	**7** 1	■	**8** 3	**9** 8	■	■	**10** 1	6	■	**11** 2	■
12 6•7	2	**13**	■	**14** 1	**15** 3	**16** 0	0	■	**18** 5•0	**20** 2
21 2	■	**22** 1	**23** 3	■	**24** 2•4	■	**25** 7	2	■	0
■	■	■	**26** 3	**27** 1	3	6	**29** 1	2	■	■
31 7	**32** 0	■	3	■	■	1	■	**33** 6	**34** 7
35 Levels 1 & 2 2	5	■	4	■	■	5	■	**36** 5	2
Levels 2 & 3	■	**37** 4	5	**38** 6	**39** 7•6	**40** 8
Levels 2, 3 & 4 **41** 7	■	**42** 3	2	**43** 1	0	■	**44** 1	**45** 9	■	**46** 2
Levels 3, 4 & 5 **47** 4	**48** 5	6	■	**49** 5	8	9	**50** 0	■	**51** 9	**52** 9	1
Levels 4, 5 & 6	**53** 0	■	4	9	■	**54** 1	**55** 8	■	0
Levels 5, 6 & 7 **56** 5	■	**57** 7•8	■	**58** 6	7	■	**59** 3	3	■	**60** 7

How to Dazzle at Maths Crosswords Book 1

Crossword 5
answers

Column headers (left to right): Levels 1 & 2 · Levels 2 & 3 · Levels 2, 3 & 4 · Levels 3, 4 & 5 · Levels 4, 5 & 6 · Levels 5, 6 & 7

						Levels 1 & 2	Levels 2 & 3	Levels 2, 3 & 4	Levels 3, 4 & 5	Levels 4, 5 & 6	Levels 5, 6 & 7
¹4	■	²1	³3	■	⁴3	5	■	⁵2	0	■	⁶4
■	⁷1	■	⁸1	⁹1	■	■	¹⁰2	5	■	¹¹1	■
¹²6•9	3	■	■	¹⁴1	¹⁵2	¹⁶3	4	■	¹⁸3	5	²⁰0
²²3	■	²³1	4	■	²⁴5•2	■		²⁵2	5	■	7
■			²⁶1	²⁷3	5	7•8	²⁹5				
³¹3	³²5	■		2	■		0	■		³³5	³⁴6
³⁵5	6	■		2	■		0	■		³⁶5	6
(Levels 2 & 3)	■		³⁷1	³⁸2	³⁹3	4•5	⁴⁰7				
⁴¹1	■	⁴²6	0	■	⁴³1	4	■	⁴⁴2	⁴⁵0	■	⁴⁶6
⁴⁷5	⁴⁸6	7	■	⁴⁹5	9	1	⁵⁰9	■	⁵¹3	⁵²6	0
■	0	■	⁵³6	4	■		⁵⁴2	⁵⁵6		4	
⁵⁶4	■	⁵⁷2	4	■	⁵⁸7	8	■	⁵⁹4	4	■	⁶⁰1

Row labels (top to bottom, left margin): Levels 1 & 2 · Levels 2 & 3 · Levels 2, 3 & 4 · Levels 3, 4 & 5 · Levels 4, 5 & 6 · Levels 5, 6 & 7